HONOURABLE CONQUESTS

By the same author

The Man Who Disobeyed:
Sir Horace Smith-Dorrien and his enemies.

Sir John Monash

The Kaffir Wars 1779-1877

Toby

Dornford Yates: A biography

Combined Forces

A New Excalibur:
The development of the Tank 1909-1939

Rude Mechanicals:
An account of Tank maturity
during the Second World War.

HONOURABLE CONQUESTS

An account
of the enduring work
of the
ROYAL ENGINEERS
throughout the Empire

by
A. J. Smithers

Leo Cooper
London

First published in Great Britain in 1991 by
LEO COOPER
190 Shaftesbury Avenue, London WC2H 8JL
an imprint of Pen & Sword Books Ltd
47 Church Street, Barnsley, South Yorkshire

ISBN 0 85052 725 2
Cataloguing in Publication data
is available from the British Library

Typeset by Yorkshire Web, Barnsley, South Yorkshire
Printed in Great Britain by The Redwood Press, Melksham

By adverting to the dignity of this high calling, our ancestors have turned a savage wilderness into a glorious empire: and have made the most extensive, and the only honourable conquests, not by destroying, but by promoting the wealth, the number, the happiness of the human race.

Edmund Burke: Speech at a County Meeting of Buckinghamshire, 1784.

CONTENTS

ACKNOWLEDGMENTS

The idea for this book, a single-volume chronicle of some of the most important work of the Royal Engineers away from the battlefield, came from the Secretary of the Institution, Colonel Gerald Napier. He has been kind enough to read it in its various drafts, but that does not mean that he bears any responsibility for the contents.

For these I have to thank the Corps Library at Chatham; in particular Mrs Margaret Magnuson and her assistant Mrs Vivien Barker. No Sapper has ever done anything anywhere at any time but Mrs Magnuson knows about it; and she has most generously given of her knowledge and her time to an outsider with no claim upon either. The book could not have been written without her help. Whether any possible reader will be grateful I cannot tell. But I am. Very.

On the sections dealing with subjects as diverse as a canal in Canada, the damming of rivers in India and digging a notable hole in Dover, I have received more help than I deserve from ladies and gentlemen who really know about these things. The President of the Ontario Historical Society, Mr. John Bonser, is also the Superintendent of the Rideau Canal. He was good enough to introduce me (by post, of course) to Dr Robert F Legget, O.C., of Ottawa, the greatest living authority on Colonel By and his works. Dr Legget has been to great pains to prevent me from falling into error and has allowed me to quote from his locus classicus, *Rideau Waterway*. Mrs Beth Hill, of Victoria B.C., has added much to my inadequate knowledge of British Columbia, has traced me there a namesake if not an ancestor, and has kindly allowed me to use portions of her fine book *Sappers*. Moving on to India, I have had help of inestimable value on the works of Sir Arthur

Cotton from gentlemen who speak with the highest authority. Major-General R. M. Rau, A.V.S.M., was, before his retirement, the Indian Army's Chief Engineer for Eastern Command and has written much on the subject. Mr. K. V. Srinivasa Rao was, not long ago, Chief Engineer (Irrigation) for Andhra Pradesh. Both of them have been generous with their help and I cannot sufficiently thank them. On Australia, I am indebted to Dr John Playford of Adelaide University for filling in some of the many gaps in my knowledge about Sapper activity down under.

The Libraries of Canada House and the India Office have been laid under contribution. As always, I have been treated not merely with courtesy but with an eagerness to help that is much appreciated. Equally have Karen James and Sarah Gray of the University of Kent at Canterbury put themselves to more trouble than I had any right to expect in order to find missing pieces for my puzzle. Their only reward, if such it be, is my gratitude.

Every author needs a candid friend, one who can tell him firmly that those passages of which he is proudest have got to be deleted and pointing out matters that ought to have been included but are not. I count myself fortunate in having for that purpose Major Derek Poulsen. After 50 years which hold quite a lot of shared experience, he knows exactly what to do; such debts can be mentioned but never paid.

In spite of all the foregoing there are bound to be mistakes and omissions. These, even though I cannot immediately identify them, are mine alone and I share them with no man.

The author and publishers are much indebted to the Director of the Royal Engineers Museum, Chatham, not only for providing most of the illustrations used in this book but also for permission to reproduce them. The drawings by Thomas Burrowes of the Rideau Canal were kindly provided by the Ontario Archives, Toronto. The relative serial numbers are given in the captions. The photograph of the light-well inside the Grand Shaft was taken by Mr Andrew Denyer and is reproduced with his kind permission.

FOREWORD
by Colonel Gerald Napier,
Director, the Royal Engineers Museum, Chatham

"Soldiers, — I have come to say to you a few kind words of parting. You are going to a distant country, not, I trust, to fight against men, but to conquer nature; not to besiege cities, but to create them; not to overthrow kingdoms, but to assist in establishing new communications under the sceptre of your own Queen."

When Sir Edward Bulwer-Lytton, Secretary of State for the Colonies, thus addressed the so-called Columbia Detachment of Royal Engineers as they embarked for their adventures on the West Coast of Canada in 1858 he might have been speaking for all the remarkable men who are the subject of this book.

The continuing story of the Royal Engineers has three strands. Foremost is that of the soldier-engineer supporting the Army in the field. It can be found in most accounts of battles, for in most the Sapper was there, often spearheading an attack or securing a withdrawal. Not for nothing have fifty Victoria Crosses been won by Sappers for feats as epic as commanding the defence of Rorke's Drift or as poignant as volunteering to remain in a collapsing tunnel to succour wounded comrades in the underground war in Flanders.

The second strand of the story tells of the Sapper as an inventor — ingenious adaptor of technology and science. In the age of burgeoning discoveries, Sappers made it their business as they do today to understand and exploit new ideas. Innovative building technology was applied to the construction of barracks, fortifications and public buildings; the Sappers' early grasp of the principles of electricity and of diving techniques led to the development of submarine mining systems, the introduction of searchlights and the world's first guided torpedo. Sappers were in the air for fifty years before the RAF, forming the first air unit in 1911. They ran signals for the Army until 1920, developed steam transport and helped give birth to the tank. The commander of the Tank Corps at Cambrai was a Sapper.

To many, however, it is the third strand that provides the most enthralling tale. In 1820 the Corps provided nearly half the country's qualified engineers. As a result, their expertise was in great demand throughout the Empire and in other spheres of British influence for bringing the necessities of civilization. Much was expected of them in countries rich in natural resources but devoid of normal communications or comforts of modern life. They responded with feats approaching genius and made their mark not only in permanent monuments of stone and steel but also in the economic and social benefits they created in the communities where they worked. It required a special independence of character and sense of mission. They seem to have been aware that they were creating history but at the same time took it in their stride as if it were no more that the normal way of proceeding.

This three-stranded story of the Royal Engineers can be seen in the exhibits at the developing Royal Engineers Museum at Chatham. A rich and varied collection includes relics of most major campaigns such as the map used by Wellington at Waterloo, devices used by the Sappers in war to defeat the enemy, the only surviving example of the world's first guided torpedo, a glorious collection of Chinese court dress presented to General Gordon and much more. It is right and proper that the remarkable feats of the honourable conquerors, to adapt the title of this book, should now be revealed not only in the Museum but also by an author who is able to do them justice.

PROLOGUE

THE CORPS OF ROYAL ENGINEERS, though granted that title as recently as 1787, justly claims Norman ancestors. The most famous of King William's Engineers were the knight Humphrey de Tilleul and the monk Gundulph of Bec. Gundulph, having presumably learnt his trade somewhere in the Church, accompanied the Conqueror to Pevensey. Sieur Humphrey, afflicted with wife trouble, remained behind: his immortality is secured by a place in the Bayeux tapestry. Brother Gundulph, immune from such distractions, designed and built the White Tower as the central feature of his master's new fortress of London and was later enthroned as Bishop of Rochester. His memorial, in stone, can be seen any day. Impressive though such a pedigree has to be, I venture to suggest that the Corps may well possess roots that go far deeper and are no less illustrious.

For a period as long as that separating the reigns of two Elizabeths a Roman army of three Legions garrisoned England. At any given moment they would have carried on their muster-rolls the names of some 20,000 regular soldiers; the arrivals and departures over nearly four centuries would have totted up to a very considerable number and many old soldiers on discharge settled down here with their British-born wives and children. Their enduring work remains, the Wall that strides across Rome's North-West Frontier and is still recognizable after nearly two thousand winters and summers. These men were the mightiest military engineers of all, their feats only being surpassed in times little beyond our own memories. Half a century before Christ, the Tenth Legion was boasting, probably justly, that it could, at a moment's notice, throw a bridge over any known river, beginning by felling and shaping the necessary trees from any nearby forest. In winter quarters when under-employed, any working party picked at random could build an ocean-going ship, including the forging of all its ironwork. The boasts were justified over and over again. Making the roads that run arrow-straight across the Staff maps of western Europe was all a part of their ordinary duty. The stone bridges encountered by Wellington's men in Portugal and Spain, put there by men in the pay of the Emperor Augustus, looked — and still look — as if the masons had only walked off the site last week. The Royal Engineer wears two reminders of this: 'Quo fas et gloria ducunt', by interpretation 'To wherever honour and glory lead' and, more laconically, 'Ubique', or 'Everywhere'. He may very well also have running in his veins some infusion of Roman blood. Certainly, both the Legions and the Corps seem to have built for eternity.

In continental Europe the business of military engineers has always been to plan and then construct the fortifications of cities and other defended places. Having perfected their own, they addressed themselves to compassing the destruction of the works of rival practitioners. Siegecraft was their particular study and, over the centuries, it developed into a highly sophisticated business. In England, using the word as a Frenchman would, there was little need of such mysteries. Domestic sieges could usually be brought to a successful conclusion by turning off the water and accelerating results by a little thoughtful bribery. The Norman castle and its successors — King Richard's Chateau Gaillard, high over the River Seine at Les Andelys was probably the most perfect specimen, though our own Dover has worn better — represented the high tidemark of the military engineer's art. When the last of these had been built, demand for his services almost ceased until the arrival of the siege-gun in the mid-15th century. With the breaching of the walls of Byzantium (and the beginning of the Renaissance) by the great gun made by the renegade Hungarian engineer Urban, the nature of static war changed completely; new forms of defensive works were needed and from such demand came the beautiful creations of Sebastien le Prestre de Vauban and his peers at about the time of the English Restoration. England was fortunate enough to need no walled cities, save only for Berwick-upon-Tweed. It was upon the Navy under the Providence of God, that she relied for her security. Satisfactory though this was, it meant that the Army owned hardly any trained engineers.

When the great continental wars began the Duke of Marlborough had to make do with what little he could find. Somehow he managed, but a century later the campaigns of the Army's other Duke, Wellington, came near to foundering in Spain for lack of trained Sappers. For neither the first nor the last time it was the young men who took the business by the scruff. An excellent Academy at Woolwich had turned out subalterns painstakingly instructed in all contemporary engineering business, though they were woefully few in numbers. These became the men who, training their soldiers as they went along, furnished the Duke in the last stages of that war with a small but thoroughly competent corps of sappers and miners. Some of them, like John Fox Burgoyne and Charles Pasley, lived to enjoy rank and high reputation. Others, like Mulcaster, Holloway, Stanway and Gips, died in the breach of a stormed city, leading their infantry into the gap as Sapper officers should.

After Waterloo, as after every war, the Army melted visibly away. The Duke, determined to keep as much as he could in existence, hid it in the Colonies. From the standpoint of the Royal Sappers & Miners this was entirely satisfactory, for there was plenty of work to be done which they alone could tackle. Of the great tracts of land coloured pink in the atlas many were sparsely populated but had little attraction for settlers in search of new lives along with their families. Much of Canada, for example, appeared unchanged since the fourth day of Creation. India and Egypt, both of them ancient civilizations that were for the time being and in some sense British responsibilities, had fallen upon evil days and in some parts demanded relief from starvation. Australia and New Zealand had nothing like enough inhabitants of the kind favoured by British governments and the same could be said of South Africa. At home the post-war government reckoned the 13 million or so residents to be more than these islands could comfortably accommodate. In the interests of both home and colonies many of them should be persuaded to emigrate. There were volunteers willing enough in spirit but unenthusiastic about living in wildernesses.

In 1815 the entire engineering strength of the Army was made up of 200 regular officers and ten companies of Sappers and Miners. It was hardly an excessively large number of men for the task of introducing a substantial part of the earth's surface to the Nineteenth Century. This book attempts to chronicle, amongst other things, how these few highly-trained professionals managed to civilize, in the proper sense of the word, much of the British Empire and that greatly to the advantage of those who lived in it.

Their first charge, on arrival in some country of which only the outer rim was known, usually took the form of surveying lands never before mapped out. This was work at which the British engineers excelled all others, for it was customary that every young officer on leaving the Academy should spend six months with Ordnance Survey. This organization was to become so very big and very technical that it demanded (and has received) a history of its own. In a book such as this there can be no place for more than a bare mention. Its existence, however, provided a pool of trained and experienced people with a high reputation worldwide. The boundaries between Canada and a none-too-friendly United States owed their acceptance in large part to the respect in which young Sapper officers were held by often suspicious opposite numbers.

In very different parts of Canada and over several decades the Royal Engineers took on tasks varying from the building of the Rideau Canal, connecting Kingston with the Ottawa River as a defensive measure, to the opening up of the Cariboo goldfields in British Columbia and the founding of cities. Above all, the capital of a mighty nation, Ottawa itself, began, unassumingly enough, as an engineer encampment. Canals of another kind were desperately needed to keep the inhabitants of Southern India from death by famine when the monsoons failed. It was an engineer officer who devoted the greater part of his life to bringing about the great schemes of irrigation that saved millions from the slow death of starvation. Later in the same century another officer of the same discipline was chiefly responsible for resurrecting the rotted barrage on the Nile and bringing water to the parched fields of Egypt. South and West Australia likewise saw what the military engineer could do in the way of laying out parcels of empty land and making them fit for men and women to inhabit. All these achievements deserve to be remembered in the same way as Edmund Burke told of an earlier generation in his famous 1784 speech. 'Our ancestors have turned a savage wilderness into a glorious empire: and have made the most extensive, and the only honourable, conquests not by destroying but by prompting the wealth, the number, the happiness of the human race'. Certainly it is seldom that so much has been created by so few.

These exploits overseas were matched by activity at home. In the days before great firms of civil engineering contractors existed, Governments in need of work being done on the grand scale naturally turned to their military engineers. The first of the great Kensington Museums, the Royal Albert Hall and Wormwood Scrubs Prison all owe their existence to the Corps. The pioneers of photography would not have progressed far without the chemical research of Captain (later Sir) William Abney, R.E. The Channel Tunnel might well have been open in time for Queen Victoria's Jubilee had matters been left to Colonel Beaumont and Captain English, both lately R.E., and had not the money run out. Another sapper officer, Sir Edmund Du Cane, had more to do than any other man in reforming the penal system. Nor is this anything like a complete catalogue of all that the Corps of Royal Engineers contributed to the common good in Georgian and Victorian times. There is much still to be chronicled.

I shall no doubt be upbraided for introducing a number of characters who had the misfortune not to belong to the Corps. I acknowledge my guilt but claim some mitigating circumstances. As Hamlet is reckoned difficult to perform without the Prince of Denmark, so equally would it be with him alone. Being East Anglian born, I could not think of telling how Adelaide was founded without some account of the adventures of Colonel William Light from Theberton. Some divagations are, admittedly, self-indulgence. The Pig War with the United States has not all that much to do with the career of Major-General Palmer but I could not resist some mention of it. A thorough exegesis of Ned McGowan's war (an established piece of British Columbian folk memory) was tempting, for it is the stuff of high comedy with more than bit-parts for members of the Corps. On editorial orders, promptly obeyed by all authors, I resisted temptation. Probably that agreeable eccentric Rob Roy McGregor does not carry the story far forward but he does, to my mind, furnish useful and illustrative background material. And so on.

One last thing should be borne in mind throughout. The Sapper never has been, is not, nor will ever be a mere civil engineer in a red coat. First and always he is a combatant soldier; had it been otherwise sappers could never have been sent to execute work in places where the rifle might be as necessary as the shovel. It has been the Empire's good fortune always to be able to command a sufficiency of men handy with both. The result is that today's Royal Engineer has inherited high respect and admiration in consequence of the feats of his predecessors. No matter what great tinkerings and mutilations await the British Army his place in the Order of Battle is surely secure.

A Note on Titles

The Corps of Engineers was constituted on 26 May, 1716, the 'Royal' prefix being granted in 1787. It consisted of officers only. A few months later the Corps of Military Artificers was formed, its style being changed in 1812 to the Royal Sappers & Miners; this continued until 17 October, 1855, when both Corps were united under their present title of The Royal Engineers. In 1862, following the Mutiny, all British officers and NCOs of the three Presidency Engineer Corps of the East India Company were taken on its strength.

Then there was that elusive body of trained engineers, the Royal Staff Corps. In order to grasp its raison d'etre, some understanding of the structure of the British Army before the year 1855 is necessary. Its departmental head was the Secretary for War, whose responsibilities included all military operations as well as everything to do with Colonies. He should not be confused with the Secretary at War (an office assumed in 1809 by the 25 year old Lord Palmerston) who had charge of all the money side of the business. The senior soldier, the Commander in Chief, reigned, from his office in the Horse Guards, over the cavalry and infantry of the Regular Army but over nothing else. The Home Office put in a claim, hotly contested, to ownership of the Militia, the Yeomanry and all the Volunteer Corps. The Royal Artillery acknowledged no chief save the Board of Ordnance which lived in Palace Yard. In the words of Philip Guedalla, 'Bewildered Engineers, who owned allegiance to the Master-General of the Ordnance, had, by a pleasing anomaly, no authority whatever to command their own subordinates, the Military Artificers, and competed briskly with a Staff Corps formed by the Commander-in-Chief for the performance of precisely the same duties.' This was the Royal Staff Corps, whose most notable feat was building the Royal Military Canal across the Romney Marsh. The 'splendid anarchy' — Guedalla again — was completed by the presence of a Treasury which 'kept a distracted eye upon the services of transport and supply, commanded a vague host of store-keepers and master-bakers, and through its Commissaries governed the Commissariat'*. Until its disappearance in recent times the War Department has always tried not to fall below this high standard.

*An exegesis of all this appears in his *Palmerston* (Benn, 1926).

I

The Opening of The Shop

WHEN, A LITTLE WHILE AGO, it was deemed necessary to build an elaborate airfield in the Falkland Islands the Government unhesitatingly turned the work over to a consortium of the great civilian contracting firms. It had nearly happened once before: in the early months of 1940 Mr. Hore-Belisha, then Secretary for War, seriously suggested bringing in Costains and McAlpines to design and build the line in France that he may have wanted to bear his name. It was not always so. Before there was anything remotely like the modern construction industry the Army took care of such things and much more, from within its own resources.

The immediate combat arms, the horse, foot and guns, had little with which to occupy themselves between wars, save only to remain in being and to carry out small police operations both at home and in the colonies. Their training was of an unsophisticated kind which officers who had paid good money for their commissions could learn as they went along. Though these were the troops most commonly on view, and by far the most ornamental, there was another branch of the service little seen by the taxpayer who maintained them all. Sir Arthur Conan Doyle put his own words into the mouth of Napoleon on the subject. When the young Brigadier Gerard annoyed him by an excessive swagger, the Emperor cut him down. 'Have done with this nonsense, or you will find yourself transferred to the sappers where you will have harder work and duller plumage.' Both Sir Arthur and Bonaparte knew what they were talking about, for France was long pre-eminent in the art of the military engineer. To this day many technical terms are anglicized versions of French words. Their army still calls its sappers *'Le Genie'* and decrepit men can remember the famous music hall song of La Gouloue, *'Rien n'est sacré à un sapeur'*.

Their arts, of course, were well understood long before either England or France were known by those names. There are fascinating examples of engineering feats in the ancient world but it is not in this book that they will be found. The Roman Army is not all that distant from us in time and the Legions garrisoned these islands for a period as long as that which separates us from the Reformation. This wonderful organization produced the first regular corps of military engineers and their work remains as something at which to marvel. Beautifully made bridges, seen at their best in Spain, look as fresh as on the day when the last labourer was paid off and they bear motor traffic as easily as ox-carts. Buildings, for the most part, are long gone but the roads, where they can be found, justify the work that went into them. Arrow-straight, a regulation 20 feet wide and built to specification with mortared foundation beds, layered concrete and paved surfaces, they defy time. Even when hurried, as during Suetonius Paulinus' Anglesey campaign, the work was not scamped. Parallel trenches, the standard distance apart, were dug out, a foot of loose soil removed and replaced with large rocks, covered again with smaller ones and finally topped with a thick layer of pebbles and flint. There must be something in the Latin blood for, after a couple of millenia, Italians are still the world's best road builders. Their recent handiwork is to be seen in many former British African colonies.

One factor distinguished the early English sapper from his continental opposite number. Warfare in England seldom, if ever, demanded the planning and construction of elaborate defences for whole towns: in consequence it was not necessary to give careful study to the means of besieging them. The Norman castle was certainly the creation of engineers of the highest quality but it was not the same. Again the brains were more often than not French brains, for this was not a native English thing. Richard the Lion Heart's great Chateau Gaillard at Les Andelys on the Seine was probably the finest example of the castle builder's art, though this did not save it from falling to the wiles of other Frenchmen. Certainly there were fortified towns elsewhere; the story of the Thirty Years War tells much about them in Germany, but it was not until the arrival of Vauban that the business was elevated to both an art and a science.

Nevertheless the English, in their own fashion, trained a corps of military engineers and trained it well. Marlborough, as everybody knows, laid siege to towns and took them without recourse to the usual aids of starvation or bribery. Only after his death, however, did a British government decide that it must have its sapper officers given a proper professional training. The aspirants were, on the whole, unlikely to be the kind of men who would buy themselves a pair of Colours, serve for as long as might amuse them and then sell their commissions as if they were stocks and shares. The engineer officer needed a different cast of mind, with no aversion from figures and willing to make a career for himself. In order to turn the bright young men into an English *Genie* it was a Hanoverian monarch, King George II, who signed the Warrant that is the Corps of Engineers' root of title. The date was 30 April, 1741, at a time when the entire Army was in a lamentable condition from long neglect. Very probably it came just in time to prevent something like disintegration into a few under-strength regiments of horse and foot with precious little else. The motive power behind it came from the Duke of Montagu, Master-General of the Ordnance, whose office continued until 1938. From that day forth the ultimate power in the Corps rested with the Master-General of the time. The Warrant does not flatter the sappers of the 1740s: '. . . it would conduce to the good of the service if an Academy or School was instituted, endowed, and supported for instructing the raw and inexperienced people belonging to the Military branch of this office in the several parts of Mathematics necessary to qualify them for the service of the Artillery and the business of the Engineers: and that there is a convenient room at Woolwich Warren, which is our property, and may be fitted up for that purpose'. In this fashion came into being the famous Royal Military Academy, never called other than 'The Shop'. Part of the building consisted of a tower, all that remained of a house once belonging to Prince Rupert. His over-excitable military ideas are unlikely to have been held up as an example to the cadets.

These young gentleman, and they were mostly of no more than public school age, were from the beginning paid, clothed and housed at Government expense. To secure a place it was necessary to be nominated by the Master-General. Once in, the cadet was treated as an officer throughout his time of instruction and subjected to a public examination before being given his commission. Not surprisingly, for this was not the best period of any part of the Army, discipline was slack and the examination a formality. Vacancies did not occur with the regularity that could have been wished — the Navy toast to 'A Bloody War Or A Sickly Season' had its equivalent ashore — and in consequence many cadets grew tired of waiting and joined the East India Company service. The Company's own college at Addiscombe did not open until 1809. The bloody war came with the year 1756 and everything to do with The Shop was tightened up. In its aftermath, in 1764, Lieutenant-Colonel James Pattison was appointed to be in fact, if not name, Commandant with wide powers. Pattison took the Academy by the scruff, compelling the cadets to cut down, if not to give up, their excessive drinking, to attend lectures and drills and to take their careers with proper seriousness. The masters, civilians all, were made to give up such little enterprises as private coaching for outsiders and taking bribes for allowing the undeserving to pass the examinations. Inevitably, in future years, The Shop would run into bad patches but after Pattison it became a thoroughly competent training ground for the technical Corps. The Professors were to be the cream of their kind, though for the most part they were of foreign nationality. The famous M. Landmann, who held office for 38 years, had previously been Professor of Fortification and Artillery at the Ecole Royale Militaire in Paris. His assistant, Herr Blumenheben, had been in the service of one of the German kingdoms. Their great ability rubbed off on to the young men, as the subsequent exploits of many of them proclaim.

Pattison's Rules and Regulations tell us of what they learned in their years at Woolwich. A few extracts may be in point:

6. The Professor of Fortification and Artillery shall teach practical geometry and mathematics, particularly applied to the raising and transporting of heavy weights, the art of surveying and levelling, with their application to the conveying of water or draining morasses.

7. He shall teach the science of fortification in all its parts, with

the manner of attacking and defending places, as likewise the use, conduct and direction of mines.

8. He shall teach the rudiments of military architecture, particularly the method of making plans, elevations and sections of powder magazines, guard rooms, barracks, storehouses, and other buildings that may be necessary in fortified towns.

9. He shall teach the theory of artillery, viz. the doctrine of projectiles, so as to apply the same to gunnery, the principles on which the several pieces of ordnance and their carriages are constructed, and the method of forming exact draughts of the same, according to the tables used by the office of ordnance; likewise the names, uses and dimensions of all other engines and implements of war.

11. The Professor of Mathematics shall teach the principles of arithmetic, algebra, the elements of geometry, the mensuration of superficies and solids, plane trigonometry, the elements of conic sections, and the theory of perspective, as also geography and the use of the globes.

13. The Drawing Master shall teach the method of sketching ground, the taking of views, the drawing of civil architecture, and the practice of perspective.

14. The Writing Master shall perfect the gentleman cadets in writing, and qualify them in arithmetic as far as the rule of three.

On top of these things the cadets were thoroughly grounded in Latin and French. As they progressed upward the teaching became more and more advanced. By the time he reached the Third Class the cadet would have mastered cube roots and quadratic equations, along with Caesar's Commentaries, Ovid and Sallust. He could draw 'Larger and more difficult landscapes, coloured' and had begun the art of surveying. In the Fourth and final Class the mathematics part engrossed 'Mechanics applied to the raising and transporting heavy bodies, together with the use of the lever, pulley, wheel, wedge and screw etc.', along with 'The laws of Motion and Resistance, Projectiles and Fluxions'. Under Captain Smith, who arrived in 1772, the tightening-up process went even further. Monthly reports were called for on every cadet and the final examination was something to be dreaded. Inevitably many of the young men found the whole business beyond them and faded out. Those who stuck it out were not all that numerous, for the records show that the numbers at any one time never exceeded about 50. To make sure that they went into the world as gentlemen as well as cadets they were also provided with a dancing master.

As has always happened throughout the long history of the British Army the painstaking education given to its prospective officers during the years of peace had to be much attenuated as war succeeded war. In 1783, at the end of the American war, there were so many unemployed artillery officers that they were posted to the engineers and left few vacancies for The Shop to fill. Ten years later the long series of wars with France began and the pendulum swung once more. So great was the demand for officers that the public examination was suspended and commissions could be had for little more than the asking. There had never been a fixed length of time for the Cadet to undergo a course of instruction at the Academy. When he felt ready to be examined, he presented himself; should he fail to pass he would have more chances, up to a maximum number which varied from time to time. If he failed too often he would be turned out. The Inspector complained to the Master–General that standards were falling sharply in consequence of the new war; this was a fact of life to be repeated as war followed war until recent times. No doubt some sub–standard officers did reach the engineers as they did every other corps but they cannot have been many or significant. Colonel Fletcher's lines of Torres Vedras, of which more later, was a defensive system of such excellence that even Massena praised it; and the beautiful little Fort Concepcion, standing in the middle of nowhere in northern Portugal after shrugging off attempts to blow it, still proclaims that the British army was there.

The Industrial Revolution had not, so far, done much for the military engineer. A man minded to travel from, say, Rome to London in 1815 would have had to resign himself to taking as long over the journey as Julius Caesar. The mechanical aids to construction, wheel, screw–jack, pulley–block, lever and wedge had been in use since unrecorded times along with the pick, shovel and barrow. Only blasting powder had been added to the equipment of Waldivius Ingeniator, the Conqueror's engineer and reputed founder of the Corps. With nothing but these relics of antiquity to help them, young men from The Shop performed feats worthy to stand beside those of the sappers of Rome and Normandy.

No engineer, however talented, can achieve much without a competent labour force. Until modern times most armies depended for this upon temporary hirelings picked up locally as best could be managed and eked out by grumbling infantrymen. It was not until 1772 that the first company of soldier-artificers was raised, and it was raised in Gibraltar. Their value was demonstrated during the Great Siege and their work, enlarged and improved by a new generation of sappers — this time Canadian — under Lord Gort remains for all to see and admire. The demand for a permanent engineering corps became irresistible and in 1797 it appeared in the Army List. In the nature of things there were never enough men to satisfy every demand but from Torres Vedras to the Albert Hall this small corps has left a mark upon those parts of the atlas once coloured pink with which no other military body can compare. It is time to take a look at some, though by no means all, of its doings.

II

Further Education: General Pasley and The Royal School of Military Engineering

TWO GENERATIONS AGO the philosopher Dr Angelo Rapaport wrote* that 'In the course of my studies, historical researches and literary exhumations . . . I have been struck by the fact that the pages of history are full of the splendid deeds and achievements of sons of sin, of children born out of lawful wedlock'. He went on to catalogue a few: Erasmus, Charles Martel, Dunois of Orleans, Leonardo da Vinci, Don John of Austria the victor of Lepanto, and Francisco Pizarro, along with a dozen or so lesser folk. Had his reasearches travelled in that direction he might also have listed two of the most illustrious Sapper officers of them all. One of them is known to everybody with an interest in the Army. John Fox Burgoyne — the 'Fox' came from having Charles James for a Godfather — was the offspring of that General Burgoyne who was variously known as Gentleman Johnny or Handsome Jack and the opera singer Susan Caulfield. The General, having been taken prisoner at Saratoga and released in exchange for 1,047 Americans, arrived back in England in February, 1782; John Fox was born later in the same year. His legal status as 'filius nullius' bothered neither him nor anybody else, for he lived to be present at all the great battles of the Crimean War and died both Field-Marshal and baronet at the time when Bismarck was founding his German Empire at Versailles. Burgoyne's is one of the half-dozen very great names among Royal Engineers. Along with Gordon and Kitchener he has a statue in London, his being hard by the Athenaeum and in calling distance of that of Sir John Franklin for whom he had once built a portable boat to be used

* In his *Splendid Sons Of Sin,* Stanley Paul, 1928.

15

in his Arctic explorations. Sociably near also is that other Sapper magnifico, Lord Napier of Magdala.

Equally famous within his Corps, but practically unknown outside it, is the name of General Sir Charles Pasley who began life under the same difficulty. Two years before Burgoyne was born, a border laird turned London merchant and also named Charles Pasley unexpectedly found himself father to a son. The experience lacked novelty, for he already had three, along with the same number of daughters. The difference was that Mrs Pasley had no part in the business this time and the young Charles Pasley's mother was decently concealed from the inquisitive. It did not seem to matter, any more than the appearance of John Fox Burgoyne had bothered Lady Charlotte, his father's wife. Like the Burgoynes, the Pasleys were armigerous, as were their cousins and neighbours the Malcolms, and the higher orders of society know how to deal with anything. The addition to the family that occurred on 8 September, 1780, at Eskdalemuir was a small difficulty to be taken in the stride. The two families had already produced a good quota of Admirals and Generals and the boy, irrespective of from which side of the blanket he had come, might well become such a one himself. The most famous of the generation then in the saddle was Admiral Sir Pulteney Malcolm whose ubiquity throughout the long wars with both France and Mr Madison was equal to that of any sapper. He appears regularly in the memoirs of Sir Harry Smith, with whom he struck up a lasting friendship. It began on board Sir Pulteney's ship off New Orleans on a day in 1814. Smith came aboard in the line of duty and, being a little tired, accepted his host's offer, poured himself a half-tumbler of spirits ('I think it was gin') added not much in the way of water and sank it at one draught. " 'Well done,' says the Admiral, 'I have been at sea, man and boy, these 40 years, but damn me if I ever saw a stiffer glass of grog than that in my life'." It was meant as a compliment, and orders were promptly given to the steward that Major Smith was to have anything he wanted and at any time. The Malcolms and the Pasleys always understood how things should be done.

Charles Pasley was of the same breed. When he was wounded during the Walcheren Expedition in 1809 another sapper of his batch, (Mulcaster, who was to be killed in the storming of Badajoz)

16

wrote to tell their mutual friend Burgoyne what had happened. 'Our poor friend Pasley is badly wounded. He had a musket ball through his body and a bayonet stab in the thigh. He was wounded leading the storming party which carried one of the advanced works under Colonel Pack. He struck one Frenchman, disarmed a second, stabbed a third, and was attacking a fourth when he fell. What a desperate dog!' He was, in addition to all that, a young man of quite remarkable brain power.

His education was as much out of the common as everything else about him. As he could hardly be paraded in public without explanation even in tolerant border country, Charles was forced to make do with what he called 'a lassies' school'; this rudimentary instruction was supplemented by Latin, Greek and French taught by a neighbour who had been blinded by lightning off West Africa whilst serving as a ship's doctor.

Burgoyne was luckier. As Gentleman Johnny was extremely hard up his friend Lord Derby took over responsibility for John Fox and sent him to Eton. It is doubtful whether it was able to do more for him than the 'lassies' school' and the blind Mr Little; by the age of 8 young Pasley was reading the New Testament in Greek; when told that he was not yet old enough for mathematics he borrowed a book from 'the housekeeper of a neighbouring nobleman' and taught himself. For intellectual amusement at the age of 14 he wrote a 'History of the Wars of Langholm and translated it into Latin after the style of Livy. None of this detracted from the 'desperate doggery' which was always a part of him. Charles Pasley led the young roughs of Langholm in their battles against the neighbouring villages. A month before his 16th birthday, it being plainly time for him to move on, he entered The Shop.

Nothing of particular interest happened there, though he was nearly turned out for his part in some practical joke on a master. In 1797, with a long war plainly ahead, the Army could not be too intolerant of such things and at 17½ he was commissioned in the Royal Artillery, transferring later to the engineering branch. Charles Pasley had advantages from his irregular birth as well as the reverse. His aunt Magdalen had married a Colonel Dirom who was now a General, his uncle Thomas was on the way to becoming an Admiral and his brother — legitimate brother — James was also a naval officer. His cousin and exact contemporary, Charles

Malcolm, was the senior of his generation, his elder brother George having died a midshipman at 18. This is only a selection of the naval and military Malcolms and Pasleys; with such credentials young Charles had much to expect from life.

It was Uncle Thomas who directed the young gunner to give up gunnery and become a sapper. Charles had been happy enough at Brentwood with his brigade of 6-pounders but he obeyed. On 21 April, 1798, he was formally gazetted into his new Corps. He took the business very seriously, asking Uncle Thomas for books. The only ones of any use were foreign. *La Science des Ingenieurs* by M. Belidor, in 2 volumes; Tulcke's *Field Engineering,* translated from the German 'by Hewgill of the Guards', also 2 volumes: *Antoni on Artillery,* translated from the Italian. There were no English works, though, as Charles wrote, 'Mr. Telford will be able to point out to you a good book on civil architecture'. With all these in his baggage Lieutenant Pasley sailed early in 1799 for the British-held island of Minorca.

His tour of service in the Mediterranean was highly enjoyable and not over-demanding. He helped in building forts, towers and batteries along the coast, watched the fleet sail in with John Jervis, Lord St Vincent, flying his flag in the huge *Ville de Paris,* and learnt the Minorquin dialect. Officers in the French emigré regiment called Dillon's taught him their language; others in the two Swiss regiments in British pay, Rolles and de Wattevilles, taught him German and somebody else taught him Italian. Then the uses of nepotism showed themselves. General Dirom, who liked Charles Pasley, managed with difficulty to secure him a posting to Malta, where he met Burgoyne. He also caught fever and nearly managed to obtain sick leave in Egypt where Sir Ralph Abercromby's army lay. When the ship which he expected to take him suddenly filled her sails and left he sought out cousin Tom Briggs — the one who was to become Admiral — and spoke his mind. Cousin Tom took Charles to his Admiral, Sir Richard Bickerton, who promised to contrive a passage for him. There were the inevitable delays but on 22 March, 1802, Pasley embarked. The rest of his adventures during this time might have been written by Captain Marryat, so nearly do they resemble those of his Jack Easy and Peter Simple. He arrived in a merchant brig, 'commanded by a man of the most desperate and abandoned character I ever met with, whom I was even obliged to keep in order by threatening to shoot him'. This expert arrived in the dark, drove his ship ashore and announced that they were 30 miles to the west of Alexandria where they would certainly be murdered by wandering Arabs. When dawn broke and they found themselves to be actually in the harbour the master received congratulations for his skill. Not, though, from Pasley. He travelled up the Nile for 140 miles above Cairo, 'was hospitably received by the officers of the Corps,' inspected the pyramids and 'the ancient Egyptian ruins and grottoes'. There were the usual attempts at robbery and possibly murder, but Pasley was equal to that.

On 22 May he left Alexandria in a schooner, spent ten days at Rhodes and was back in Malta by mid-summer, 1802. In the course of the next year he, along with various friends not named, hired an open boat and sailed to Syracuse. As usual they received 'the greatest attention and hospitality', this time from a Mr Lecky, 'who has an estate on the site of the villa of Timoleon'. They climbed Etna in a storm, were stranded for the night in a hut, walked to Taormina and chartered another open boat to Palermo. His naval credentials had made Pasley a kind of liaison officer between the fleet and the army, but the fun was nearly over. The Treaty of Amiens, always shaky, ended and the war began again.

Charles Pasley had still some small adventures to come of a seafaring kind but there is not space enough for them. One, however, must be included. Admiral Bickerton invited him and his cousin James Malcolm to dine with Lord Nelson on board HMS *Victory*. For once Pasley does not give a date, but by inference it was early in 1804. 'Our conversation was short and commonplace and I did not sit near him at dinner, but I remarked the keenness of his look and gesture which announced the decision of his soul. He is now extremely sanguine in his expectation that the French fleet, which is ready for sea, will come out. The general supposition is that they will make a run for Egypt with troops . . . His Lordship's ardent mind is so much bent on the destruction of the enemy that he thinks and talks of nothing else'.

Pasley was becoming a person of consequence. Sir Alexander John Ball, Governor of Malta, sent him back to Sicily in order to find out whether timber could be brought down from the forests to Syracuse by canal. A letter went home demanding every possible book on waterworks, canals, aqueducts, bridges, docks and carpentry. Once more Mr Telford was asked to advise, especially on the matters of 'large roofs, great wooden buildings etc.' In his spare time he invented a system of semaphore signals, rivalling that of Sir Home Popham. No business resulted from either.

By 1806 Pasley was caught up in the affairs of Naples and the battle of Maida. This deserves more than a mispronounced Vale as its memory, for it was the equivalent of a great and successful mid-war commando raid. The French, having beaten everybody, were widely regarded as invincible, as the Germans and the Japanese were to be. The politics that led to Maida no longer matter, but the small battle does. Pasley watched Colonel Kempt (who will appear again, far from Italy) lead the charge and saw that 'The French waited the onset with the utmost firmness till the points of the bayonets almost crossed each other. They then turned their backs, to a man, as if by word of command' and ran. He sent an account to John Burgoyne in Malta. 'I attached myself to the Light Infantry, who were the first corps engaged, and had the pleasure of witnessing the famous charge in which they ran down the heroes of Marengo like a flock of sheep.' The bayonets of the redcoats had pricked the French bubble and things were never the same again.

So far Pasley had been only on the fringe of the great war, but the hardest part was near. In 1807 he was present at the attack on Copenhagen where he met Sir Arthur Wellesley for the first time. 'He is the man I should wish to see at the head of the first large British army that acts.'

For Pasley himself the culminating point of his career was not far off. The operations around Copenhagen had given him food for thought, the main course being about the state of his own Corps. There could be no room for two opinions; the siege works had not been the kind of thing one might expect from well-trained military engineers. Mere Captains, however well connected, could not do much about it, but Pasley intended to try. For immediate purposes, however, there was other work at hand. Part of the spoils of a campaign as inglorious as it had been necessary was the island of Heligoland. Pasley, the amphibian engineer, was sent to take a look at its defences and advise on them. After some small adventures in *Riddle of the Sands* country, including a brush with a French *chasse-marée* privateer, he came home and was set to work on the construction of a baker's dozen of Martello towers along the Essex coast. This, for the moment, suited him well enough. As he later admitted, the travelling on horseback gave him the chance to let the horse find its own way whilst the rider kept his nose in a book. A strictly professional book, and in a foreign language. The towers built between the mouth of the Colne and Horsey Island are, at any rate in part, Pasley's work.

The tempo, even though it was that of horse and sail, was accelerating and Captain Pasley had greatly matured. On the second anniversary of Maida, 4 July, 1808, he volunteered for service under Sir John Moore in Spain, reminding authority that he spoke the language. He would, for choice, command a battalion rather than an engineer sub-unit; were that not possible he would gladly be attached to one of the Spanish armies. In the upshot, he was ordered to take himself to Gijon, on the Biscay coast, and report to General Leith. The General held no command but had been sent to find out what was going on in the Asturias. Pasley's part was to go with the army of Don Joachin Blake, appreciate the state of affairs there and keep Leith informed. By mid-November Blake's army had been destroyed. Pasley, having written a long and thorough report on what he had seen, joined himself to Moore. There he met once again his friend Burgoyne, just in time for the retreat to Corunna.

The main business of the Engineers during that unpleasant campaign was to destroy solid bridges over rivers, and they did it very badly. Of all the attempts made only two succeeded to any degree; one was at Castra Bonzalo, where a subaltern named Davy destroyed the bridge and, through inexperience in such matters, himself with it; the other, at Benevente, was seen off by Burgoyne. If the bridges were Roman, as is quite likely, the wonder is that they managed to destroy any at all. Pasley, never a man to boast, plainly put in a little desperate doggery during the last fight, attaching himself to either the Black Watch or the West Kents; probably the latter, for their officer casualties were heavy. All he said was that 'I was in, or a witness to, most of the skirmishes during our retreat and in all the latter part of the battle of the 16th, having been in Corunna when it commenced. It was the hottest fire I ever saw, but unfortunately the ground, being intersected and in the enemy's favour, did not admit of much bayonet work.' Bayonet work is not generally reckoned sapper business but there are always those who cannot be kept away from it. Pasley brought back from Corunna two articles of faith. The British soldier, given half a chance, could beat anything the French or anyone else might bring against him. And the British military engineers were not up to their work.

Before long Captain Pasley was caught up in the worst fiasco of the war, the expedition to the island of Walcheren. He had much to say about it, but unfortunately it has no place here. His wounds were very severe, sufficiently so to make it doubtful whether he would pull through. He did, but his health was never the same and his campaigning days were over. He was just 28, and the serious work of his life was about to begin.

It started with much writing. Pasley, not being blinkered by regimental duties, had seen more than most officers of his rank. One thing had become very plain to him, and it is a lesson that recurs throughout history. At the end of a great war that has gone on for years the British Army is superb in both performance and equipment. When the King's (or Queen's) enemies have been seen off, the rump of an army forgets all the new things it has learned. It happened between the armies of Sir Douglas Haig and Lord Gort; it had happened before, between those of Marlborough and Wellington. No arm of the service had been worse affected than the engineers. Marlborough's sappers, though lacking any Shop to teach them, could have fortified a city or a mountain and could have devised ways of taking it; they could have put pontoon bridges across any river, have built more solid and permanent structures at need, have blown up anything worth blowing up and performed every other function a continental sapper could do. The handful that accompanied Sir Arthur Wellesley to Spain, for lack of both equipment and training, could do hardly any of these things. Since the putting of this to rights was nobody's business, Charles Pasley decided to take it upon himself. It is probably just as well that the campaigns in the Peninsula lasted for as long as the Second World War. By the time Sir Arthur had become Duke of Wellington he was beginning to have an engineer corps worthy of his army.

The obvious rejoinder to Pasley's condemnation would be to ask how, if the Engineers were so useless, the great Lines of Torres Vedras, which probably settled the fate of Bonaparte in

Spain, came to be constructed. Pasley himself can deal with this, in a letter he wrote just before Waterloo was fought. 'About 5 years before, I received a letter from my friend Captain Squire, one of the Engineers superintending the construction of the celebrated Lines of Torres Vedras in 1810, in which at one time no less than 7,000 Portuguese peasants were employed. After stating that he found the Royal Military Artificers almost useless, as they could not understand the simplest plan or section, and yet it was necessary, for want of better, to employ them and artificers from other Corps as overseers and foremen, he concluded by observing that efficient Engineer soldiers could never be formed out of a body of men so stupid and ignorant. I differed from that opinion so far that I ascribed their irregularities to a vicious system of discipline, and their ignorance to the want of instruction, and I had the pleasure, in little more than a year afterwards, of communicating to him the success of my efforts for the improvement of the Plymouth Company.'

Pasley's convalescence was a long one. Even as he lay half-dead in Middelburg Church, temporarily a hospital, the family kept an eye on him. Captain Elphinstone RN, whose sister was wife to Sir Pulteney Malcolm, managed to have him transferred to 'comfortable lodgings' — his cousin Mina's expression. There he wrote a long letter to Lord Chatham explaining just how a simple piece of engineering work would make it possible to insulate Flushing and make it impregnable. Curiously enough, Bonaparte had reached the same conclusion, though his plan had the added refinement of drowning the civil population. Neither was ever tried, for Flushing was evacuated and Captain Pasley took to his pen.

The great work he called *Military Policy of the British Empire* was published in November, 1810, though the early part had been written two years earlier. It was pounced upon immediately by the critics, all of whom praised it. Mr Canning, in the *Quarterly Review,* remarked that it was 'one of the most important political works that had ever fallen under the observation of the reviewer'; more to the point Pasley's friend Jones, another fine young RE officer, wrote to tell him that 'Lord Wellington reads it, Marshal Beresford reads it, in short it is universally read amongst us and as universally admired'. Jones's letter was dated six weeks before Beresford's Battle of Albuera. As the book — he called it an

'Essay', although it covered nearly 600 pages — was purely military, whatever Mr Canning might think, it has to give place here to other matters. Its importance, of course, was to make the name of Pasley widely known both in and out of the Army. Fortunately he planned for more active ways of reforming bad systems than by merely writing about them, otherwise Pasley might have become no more than a Georgian Liddell Hart. He could, and did, do better than that.

In October, 1810, at the end of his sick leave, Pasley was posted to Plymouth. What he found there horrified, but probably did not surprise, him. The Muster Rolls were full of old men and boys, the defences were ill-contrived and ill-made and, as he told cousin Mina, 'My time had been as much occupied in routing out abuses as in anything else'. By the time he had routed them out there was at least a clean slate on which to write.

It was Pasley's firm intention to educate any men put into his charge even if he had to pay for it himself. For some time he did so, the £300 a year wound pension he had been granted being most likely applied towards the cost. He was not, however, a one-man band. The younger sapper officers had for years been talking in the same terms. There is a letter from John Fox Burgoyne, headed 'Vizeu 4 April 1810,' saying that 'I am entirely on your side respecting the Corps and everything else, and feel assured we want a great deal more than I will explain to you by letter. I have been brooding over these ideas for some time myself but, meeting nobody to encourage me, or to who I dare broach my opinions, I could scarce believe I was myself sincere in them. Yours and Squire's letters have given me confidence in these ideas and made me fit for anything. I have written to sound Mulcaster and wait with impatience for his answer. I long to gain him, knowing him to be a clever fellow and, what is more, a smart, dashing, indefatigable officer.' By the time Pasley went to Plymouth, Mulcaster was dead in the breach at Badajoz.

It was useless to look in the direction of senior RE officers, even those who had done well in the American War. The young men must pull the Corps together as best they could or it would rot away. Captains Charles Lefebure, RE Officer to Stuart at Maida, was dead, killed at Matagorda during Graham's operations against Cadiz. He it was who had first opened young Pasley's eyes

24

to the true condition of things; Squire, 'my intimate friend', had been of the same mind but he too was dead, killed by sheer exhaustion in the summer of 1812. They, and others of the same generation, had met and corresponded regularly, forming what might fairly be called a school of Sapper thought. Pasley's contempt for the established order was boundless. The Shop was passing out young officers who 'had never seen a fascine or a gabion, without the smallest knowledge of the military passage of rivers, of military mining, or of any other operation of a siege, excepting what they might pick up from the French writers.'

The Shop was not to be blamed. For the first time, but by no means the last, the demands of a great war had turned the place into what we would call an OCTU. The army in the field needed Sappers, particularly Sapper officers. Half- or quarter-taught ones were better than none at all. Pasley could achieve very little in the way of officer training but his Plymouth Company, under instruction of a new kind, might leaven the non-commissioned element. He was also of sufficient standing now to be able to write letters to the highest quarters that would not be dismissed as impudence. Though invariably expressed with proper terms of respect, Pasley had misgivings, for he had already made enemies there. As he himself had remarked when about to write his book, 'I shall give great offence to all classes of men, to Ministers, to Lord Chatham and to the heads of the Corps of Engineers . . . I shall also be charged with presumption, in the dictatorial style I shall assume but when a man sets himself up against general opinions any affectation of modesty would be out of the question'. He had been right on both counts. When the letter to Lord Chatham offered to stake Pasley's own commission if he failed to raise standards, it received a civil but slightly dusty answer. He could hardly have expected anything else.

Lord Mulgrave, now Master-General, proved rather better value. As a young man he had been present at the siege of Toulon and he knew something about these matters. Pasley, considering this 'very promising', went ahead and 'took the opportunity . . . to carry into effect at my own expense a system of practical and theoretical instruction for the junior officers of the Corps of Royal Engineers and for the non-commissioned officers and privates of the department, a company of whom, then termed the Royal

Military Artificers, volunteered to work at the operations of a siege in the summer of (1811), after their regular working hours for the day were over, and they were accordingly practised in the construction of a gun and mortar battery and portions of parallels and approaches, after having previously made fascines and gabions with materials purchased in the neighbourhood.' In the evenings, and under no sort of compulsion, the men attended further classes in which they were taught practical geometry, plan drawing and elementary fortification, 'according to a course of instruction drawn up by me for that purpose'. Apart from Lieutenant Machell, who was to be killed at the siege of San Sebastian along with the Duke's favourite Sapper, Colonel Sir Richard Fletcher, Pasley himself was the only instructor. It seems highly possible that the 'lassies' school' had taught him things not studied at Eton and, quite by chance, the time was apt for reform of education in all its branches. Like so many improvements to Sapper affairs it had begun in India. Andrew Bell, a young Scottish minister, had gravitated to becoming Chaplain to the East India Company's factory at Fort St George, soon to be Madras. Not being over-employed in that capacity, Dr Bell interested himself, as nobody else seems to have done, in the simple mechanics of passing on one's knowledge to others. In his charge was the Military Orphan School where it was his duty to teach, entirely by the light of nature, classes of small European children strong neither in aptitude nor enthusiasm for learning. For want of anywhere else to go, Bell studied the native schools and found in them much to admire. The system on which they operated, later to be called monitorial, was virtually that used in large families. The master taught the big ones; the big ones taught the small ones. It seems like a blinding glimpse of the obvious, but only Madrassi schools used it. The underlying idea of doing things in this way was that every pupil had a tutor and every tutor a pupil. Dr Bell claimed, with justice, that both tutor and pupil learned faster thus than in any other way. His later life gave some proof of this for after his return home the 'Madras system' became widely adopted, especially when the new National Schools came into being. Bell died very rich, and was buried in Westminster Abbey. The other founder of the monitorial system, Joseph Lancaster, was less fortunate. His efforts had begun amongst the slum children of Southwark in a back room lent for the purpose by his father. He was just 19 and the year was 1790. By 1805 his reputation had won him the approval of George III and, with the blessing of both King and Quakers, he travelled the length and breadth of the country teaching poor children to teach each other. The result was probably inevitable. Mr Lancaster became bankrupt and had to leave for the New World in 1818. During Pasley's time with the Plymouth Company, however, both Bell and Lancaster were familiar names and there was much argument about where the credit for the monitorial system ought to go. Pasley probably cared little enough about this. The system was well tried and its application demanded no more than ordinary common sense. Publishers, printers and others engaged in the making and selling of books benefited. Charles Greville, in his Diary entry for 9 November, 1829, records the heroic efforts of Sir Walter Scott to pay off Constable's debts and adds, thoughtfully, that 'A new class of reader is produced by the Bell and Lancaster school, and this is the cause of the prodigious and extensive sale of cheap publications'. He then moves on to something nearer his heart, 'Byron's exploits, especially at Venice, seem to have been marvellous'.

Pasley, following the system, arranged his unpromising pupils in forms. First he lectured them and then, by simple question and answer, he picked out the most likely-looking of his audience. These he moved to the top of their forms and, in time, all were put to teaching the more backward ones. It demanded enormous patience, for Georgian roughs who could hardly scrawl their own names were not natural learners. Nevertheless, they were willing, tried as hard as did their teacher, and results came. In February, 1812, a surprisingly short time after it had all started, Pasley was summoned to London to explain to General Mann, Inspector-General of Fortifications, how the new idea was working out. Mann seemed well-disposed, as did the members of the Committee of Engineer Field Officers sitting at 90 Pall Mall, though some were doubtful of the wisdom of teaching soldiers too much. The proposal was floated that Pasley should expand into something far bigger, possibly at Woolwich. It sounded promising but he aimed higher than the Committee. Not merely Lord Mulgrave but Frederick, Duke of York and Commander-in-Chief, were brought into the business. Both were sensible and experienced men; they knew all about the Duke's lack of engineers, they knew Pasley by reputation and they gave him his head.

On 2 May, 1812, the Master-General's order arrived at Plymouth. Pasley was to take his Company, or part of it, by march route to Chatham and there set up his establishment. It was not before time. Little more than three weeks earlier the Duke had stormed Badajoz and opened Spain's southern gate; it had cost him 5,000 of his best infantry. This could not be done again, for any number of reasons. The Engineers would have to do better.

Pasley, still troubled by his wounds, made his own way to Brompton Barracks and there set up shop. With time on his hands waiting for the marching column to arrive, he devoted himself to writing text-books which were to remain loci classici for a long time. The Duke also had been doing some writing, about 'the expediency of adding to the Engineer establishment a Corps of Sappers and Miners', pointing out that the French had always had them with every one of their formations and adding that 'It is inconceivable with what disadvantages we undertake anything like a siege or want of assistance of this descrition'. Thanks to Charles Pasley and the other young sapper officers with whom he worked the Duke's Order of Battle would soon be more serviceable. When he came to invest and storm San Sebastian there was a full company of trained Sappers and Miners in their new red coats to demonstrate how the thing should be done. By the time the army was in France and seeking to bridge the considerable River Adour it had plenty of pontoons and experienced hands to work them. They were the first fruits of the new planting and were known throughout the army as 'Pasley's Cadets'.★

The Royal Engineer Establishment, for a long time now called The Royal School of Military Engineering, had lived and worked at Brompton Barracks since the Plymouth Company marched in. From first beginnings it took in cadets from the East Indian Company's college at Addiscombe and trained them as its own. Every young officer of the Royal Engineers, decade after decade, went through Pasley's mill and came out the better for it. The founder remained there until retirement as Major-General and KCB

★ Neither Napier nor Oman mentions Pasley's name anywhere.

in November, 1841. Should you wish for a contemporary's view of him in the 1830's the *Pickwick Papers* will provide it. 'Colonel Bulder' is quite definitely Charles Pasley.

This chronicle makes no pretence to tell of all the doings and sayings of a remarkable man; one last must, however, be included. When the war was over Pasley interested himself in blowing up some of the wrecks that littered the coast. Most were nuisances of which everybody was well rid. Blowing up Kempenfelt's *Royal George* in Spithead was a considerable technical achievement. It seems a pity that Pasley then found it necessary to apply the same treatment to Henry VIII's *Mary Rose*. For almost exactly 300 years she had been lying under her mudbank bothering nobody but she had the misfortune to be near enough to the *Royal George* for the engineers to find a use for the unexpired portion of their explosives. *Mary Rose* was, in her turn, blown up. The exploit rates only a brief note at the end of the General's biography. Presumably nobody was much interested.

The present generation may well forgive him this solitary lapse. Had Charles Pasley the elder, of Langholm, kept strictly to his marriage vows as a Scottish Presbyterian should, the history both of the Royal Engineers and the Army in general would have been very different. And less successful.

As for his son, look around Brompton Barracks and you will see his memorial. After Waterloo the demand for expertise in siege-craft inevitably fell off and was largely taken over by the teaching of architecture and surveying and engineering of a more civilian kind. The young men who went out into the wilderness and laid out great parts of the British Empire as a landlord might lay out a newly-acquired estate owed much to Sir Charles Pasley. As do we, the beneficiaries and descendants of beneficiaries, of their skill and labour.

There is neither Pasleyville nor Lake Pasley in the atlas. Only the Corps Library of the Royal Engineers at Brompton Barracks carries on his name in the Pasley Room. There, at least, he is appreciated; in a letter to the author, the present Secretary of the Institution of Royal Engineers gave its verdict: 'Pasley was behind much of the great happenings of the Nineteenth Century.'

III

Colonel By and the Defence of Canada

THE GREATEST ACHIEVEMENTS of the Royal Engineers were executed during the era of the Regency Buck and the Georgian tough. The men who built the canals of Canada and the irrigation systems of India were, as they needed to be, among the toughest of them all. It was something that came naturally in the age of bare-knuckle boxing and battlefield surgery without anaesthetics. Young Harry Smith of the Rifle Brigade watched interestedly as the doctor dug a musket ball from his ankle and was back on duty almost at once. A soldier was expected to endure suffering and hardship without complaint. The advantages of a public school education provided his officers with a willingness to put up with injustice and make no fuss about it. Having these mental attributes added to much book-learning, the Gentleman Cadet, once he had satisfied examiners, found himself to be the King's trusty and well-beloved commissioned officer. Most commonly his first employment in that state was to learn the business of the Ordnance Survey, during a six-month tour of duty in Wales. After this, one may imagine, almost anything would have been a change for the better.

One of the mysteries into which cadets at The Shop had been admitted was, as you will remember, the transporting of heavy weights. It had been obvious since, at least, the erection of Stonehenge that the best way of effecting this was to mount the objects upon something that would float and could be pushed or pulled along. The man-made waterways called canals had existed in various parts of the world since remote antiquity but it had only been during the previous half-century or so that they had suddenly become modish in England. The Duke of Bridgewater

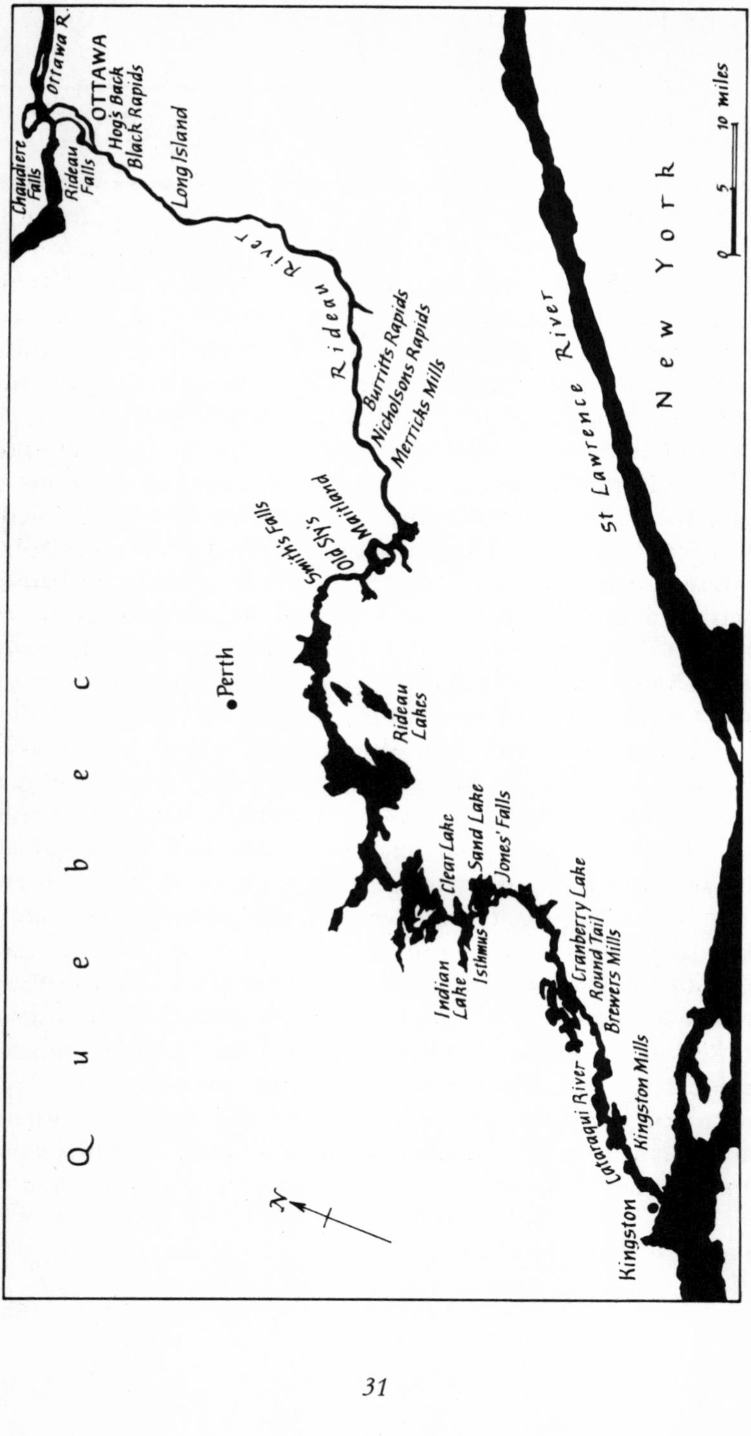
Chaudiere Falls
Ottawa R.
OTTAWA
Hog's Back
Black Rapids
Rideau Falls
Long Island
Rideau River
Burritts Rapids
Nicholsons Rapids
Merricks Mills
Maitland
Old Sly's
Smith's Falls
Perth
Rideau Lakes
Clear Lake
Sand Lake
Jones' Falls
Cranberry Lake
Round Tail
Brewers Mills
Isthmus
Indian Lake
Kingston Mills
Cataraqui River
Kingston
Q u e b e c
N e w Y o r k
St Lawrence River
N
0 5 10 miles

had begun it all in the year of the Young Pretender's march on Derby, with the object of carrying coals to Manchester. He was not the last Duke to come to the aid of the canal-builders, as will presently be told. The engineer Brindley worked out the rules of construction for navigation canals (irrigation canals are another matter altogether) and by the coming of railways there were some 3,000 miles of them in the Kingdom. The rules make simple reading but they are inflexible. The canal must run at one level except for the locks; the channel must have a flat bottom with outward sloping sides: the breadth of the bottom has to be at least double the beam of the biggest craft likely to use it and the depth at least one and a half times its draught; the area of the waterway needs to be six times the greatest midships section of it. Such criteria were not too difficult of attainment in late 18th century England. Putting them into effect in the wildest parts of Canada would not be quite the same thing, but it had become necessary well before Waterloo brought its long spell of peace to the old world. The principle of the water-borne lift cages known as locks, essential for moving vessels up and down as the ground-level changes, had long been understood. Opinions differ as to whether they had been invented by the Chinese or by Leonardo: between them they seem to have worried out everything worth inventing.

Canada had been another Norman Conquest. The ports of Honfleur and St Malo still proudly display monuments to the seamen who took their little ships across the Atlantic* carrying the hardy men who would find out exactly what this vast and unknown land was and try to introduce it to the benefits of trade. As the years went by, Canada grew in the same way that Russia had grown before her, beginning with small settlements strung out along the shores of mighty rivers. The arrival of the French and their staking-out of claims either in the beginnings of towns or in close-knit seigneuries that could be reached by water did not dispossess the native Indians to any great extent. Then, in the annus mirabilis of 1759 and under the walls of Quebec, the situation changed in a flash. The wonderful fire-discipline of Wolfe's eight regiments ruined Montcalm's army with a single volley and, for

---

* The tradition endures. In the Second World War the Royal Canadian Navy, starting with practically nothing, sent 400 fighting ships to sea.

Canada, reversed the verdict of Hastings. Britain, in the person of King George II, took over. It was fortunate that both nations derived from the same Norman root and neither preferred revolution to the rule of a regular consecrated King. The prospect of being ordered about by the despised legislators of an upstart republic offended the instincts of both of them and the coming of the Revolutionary War was not a disaster for Canada. It brought her a flood of loyal men and women, mostly British, who refused to throw off the allegiance into which they had been born: it did, however, demonstrate the extreme vulnerability of Canadian townships to attack across the St Lawrence River. The war in 1812, overshadowed on this side of the Atlantic by greater affairs in Europe, was no mere sparring match between cousins. Sir Harry Smith, on entering Washington, was ordered to burn the city to the ground, General Ross, with difficulty, persuaded Admiral Cockburn to confine his arson to the public buildings. 'I had no objection to burn arsenals, dockyards, frigates building, stores, barracks, etc., but well do I recollect that, fresh from the Duke's humane warfare in the South of France, we were horrified at the order to burn the elegant Houses of Parliament and the President house,' Smith wrote in his memoirs. The burning of Washington was an outrage. No other British army ever did such a thing anywhere else. The best that can be said was that it happened in August. Far worse had been the burning of York — now Toronto — by the Americans under Zebulon Pike in the depth of a Canadian winter.

When in doubt about anything, the Government ran to the Duke for advice. Though up to the neck in preparing for the battle of Vittoria, he gave it. There was no way of injuring the United States grievously enough to force a peace; on the other hand, 'The defence of Canada and the co-operation of the Indians depends on the navigation of the Lakes'. This meant Kingston, a base that must be made entirely secure. From this article of faith the Duke never budged. It was fortunate for Canada that the sons of Wolfe's and Montcalm's men were able to present a common front against a common enemy. The Malouins would have been more than human had they not taken some private pleasure in the five victories by American frigates over the hated Royal Navy but by now they were Canadians before they were Frenchmen. In the not impossible event of another war, the United States would have to reckon with both branches of the family of Rollo the Norseman and Duke William. Four generations later came the most recent, and probably the last, family reunion, on a beach named Juno.

The war of 1812 was ended over a dinner table, the most important of the diners being the Duke and Albert Gallatin, the highly civilised Genevese who served America as Secretary to the Treasury. For all that, there was a robust element in the States that regarded the Treaty of Ghent as ending a round rather than a fight. The feeling persisted that they had somehow been robbed of a spectacular victory. It has only been since the beginning of the present century that the platitude about war between Britain and the US being unthinkable has merited belief. It came fairly close in the early 1840s by reason of a dispute regarding the frontier between Maine and New Brunswick. Later in the same decade it came nearer still, over the Oregon boundary and with President Polk being elected on the parrot cry of 'Fifty-four forty, or fight'.★ Charles Greville's diary entry for 1 June, 1856, tells of a meeting with Thackeray, just returned from America. 'He thinks there is every probability of the quarrel (mainly about British possessions in Central America) leading to war, for there is very hostile spirit, constantly increasing, throughout the States, and an evident desire to quarrel with us . . . They are persuaded that if war ensues they will give us a great thrashing.'

Greville was relieved that the Russian war was just over, for if 'all our ships had been in the Baltic and all our soldiers in the Crimea, nothing would have prevented the Americans from seizing the opportunity of our hands being full to bring their dispute with us to a crisis'. Nearest of all, of course, was the moment in the Civil War known as the Trent affair, when the Guards were sent to Canada and it looked as if Mr. Lincoln had acquired another enemy. The last flare-up, so one hopes, came as recently as 1895, over yet another border dispute, this time between British Guiana and Venezuela. Much hard diplomacy was needed to smooth this over. When 'the longest unfortified frontier in the world' came into existence the job of finding out where on the ground lay that

★ 54° 40' North was the frontier with Russian Alaska. After a couple of years as President Mr Polk willingly settled for the 49th Parallel. It had been agreed before his time, in 1818.

part of the 49th Parallel between the Lakes and the Rockies was given to two sapper officers, Lieutenants Vavasour and Warre. That said, it is time to return to the state of affairs existing in 1815.

To regular military men it was obvious that the Americans had utterly mishandled their campaign on land and that, given better leaders and troops, another stab at Canada must surely succceed. The man who saw this most clearly was not a regular at all but he was a born soldier. Colonel 'Red George' Macdonnell was a Canadian settler who had led his militiamen in some well-planned and skilfully executed forays. He needed no telling that the proper strategy for an American army at the start of the next round would be to cut the lines of communication at Quebec and Montreal — there were no canals worth mentioning at the time — and close the St Lawrence. Upper Canada would then be effectively blockaded from the outside world. It became clear soon after the war ended that this was at last understood by the Americans.

General Jacob Brown of the US Army told Major-General Robinson early in 1815 that only the signing of the Treaty of Ghent had stopped him putting the idea into practice. Colonel Macdonnell had not waited to learn this. Whilst the battle was still going on at New Orleans 'Red George' was in his canoe personally reconnoitring a route from the strong fortress of Kingston along the river systems of the Ottawa and the Rideau. If a practicable one could be found, then Kingston would have a back entrance from Montreal that the Americans could not easily cut. He came to the conclusion that the making of a navigable waterway would be difficult but not impossible. As soon as he could, 'Red George' sketched out his plan. There would have to be a canal cut along the Rideau and Cataraqui system and it would need blockhouses at selected points for its defence. Once all that were done, Kingston should be safe. The Rideau waterway would be as much a military work as any Maginot Line.

With the war over the pace became slow, but the Colonel was not without allies. He tackled Lieut-Colonel John Harvey, DAG to the Duke of Richmond, who was then Governor-General, and, in 1818, Harvey put Macdonnell's ideas into a Memorandum on 'The Defence of the Canadas'. It was, in the ordinary way of these things, passed to the Master-General of the Ordnance. Thus it came under the eye of the Duke himself, for he currently held that office, and the Duke's answer was both prompt and friendly. It was addressed in the first instance to his own Chief, Lord Bathurst, Secretary for War and the Colonies. 'I would recommend, then, first: that the canal from Montreal to La Chine should be completed, so as to take boats of the largest size (around the St. Lawrence River — Lachine rapids at Montreal). Secondly that the navigation should be made practicable and easy to the junction of the River Rideau with the former. Thirdly that the navigation of the River Rideau should be made practical and easy to the junction with the Irish Creek, and thence, if possible, through the different lakes to Kingston . . . All these lines of navigation ought to be rendered, if possible, so perfect as that a steam vessel might be used to tow the loaded boats. Trackways should be made on which the troops might march.'

Highly desirable though all this was, the demand came at the most inauspicious moment. By 1819 England was suffering as all victorious countries do at the end of a long war. Adolf Hitler was not the first ruined dictator to go down feeling that he had planted a dart in England's vitals that might poison her entire body. The forges that had fashioned the weapons to beat Bonaparte were allowed to die down and men and women in large numbers found themselves without work. At the same time there came a great slump in agriculture, with rural distress leading to the rioting and rick-burnings that were a feature of most of the countryside. Serious people spoke openly of the possibility of revolution in the French style. One consequence of all this was a desire on the part of many people to seek a better future beyond the seas and to this the home Government was no enemy. The country, with some 13 millions of people to support, was reckoned overfull; it could only be beneficial to everybody to thin out some of them and establish a British presence in suitable and under-occupied lands. A part of the population officially described as 'redundant' became the 1820 Settlers in South Africa. Others, despairing of making a decent living in post-war Britain, made their way to Canada, Australia and New Zealand. They left with the thanks of the Government but precious little else.

There was no money in the vaults to pay for the younger sons. Once they were gone they must fend for themsleves. Canada was something of a special case, for reasons connected with more wars than one. Another factor was numbers. For every English speaker in Lower Canada there were four who spoke French. Though these were now dependant upon their own nurseries to keep up the preponderance, immigration having practically ceased, their capacity for reproduction was formidable. It took another thirty years and more before the numbers became roughly equal. Canada was far from being safe as Australia and New Zealand were safe. An unfriendly America, already possessing a large and rancorous Irish element, was casting covetous eyes on the vast emptiness that stretched towards the Rockies and the Pacific. When the ferment at home had died down and trade was running normally again, the money would have to be found to make Canada secure. But it could not be done yet.

The army was cut to the bone. Its Commander-in-Chief, the Duke, did not need to be told that the only way of keeping it in existence was to hide it in the colonies. This he did. When it came to Canada it was plain that much work of a civil engineering kind was needed and as the Royal Engineers now had little to do but train it might be politic to find useful work for them there.

There was already a small RE presence in the country, for the most part engaged in works of fortification, and with Pasley's friend Major-General Gother Mann in command. In all probablity it was Mann who, after searching for a man likely to be able to cope with difficulties not found in Europe, came up with a name. It was not a commonplace one. John By is all but forgotten in his native country. Anyone wishing to see what manner of man he was should visit Ottawa where a fine statue of him was unveiled in 1971. Though he never held higher rank than Lieutenant-Colonel nor was awarded any sort of decoration, John By's is a name of power in Canada. It came about in this fashion.

The By family originated in London and had a long tradition of Government service, mostly with the Customs. The name, which sounds pure Danish, has long died out. John By was born in 1781, the same time as Pasley and Burgoyne, and attended his period of instruction at The Shop during the Landmann era. In 1799 he was duly gazetted Lieutenant and, in accordance with the usual practice, was posted first to the Royal Artillery. Some months later, like Pasley, he contrived a transfer to the Engineers. In August, 1802, during the Peace of Amiens, he was posted to the Engineer establishment in Canada as one of the Sapper officers entrusted with the defences of Quebec. As part of his task, By, with the help of another young officer, constructed a splendid model of the entire city, including the confluence of the St Charles and St Lawrence Rivers and the site of Wolfe's battle on the Plains of Abraham. The model came back to Woolwich with him at the end of his tour and was for many years one of The Shop's most prized exhibits. It has found, very properly, its permanent home in the Canadian War Museum at Ottawa. By was a gifted model-maker; another of his creations was that of a bridge on the truss principle with a span of 1,000 feet. It met with the approval of both Charles Pasley and John Fox Burgoyne some years later. Pasley was then much occupied with bridges for the Duke's last operations. In a letter to Burgoyne treating of floating bridges made of pontoons and casks, his personal favourite for most purposes, Pasley writes of the difficulties that come when the enemy has blown up the arches of a permanent bridge but left the piers. 'A good and light temporary bridge of carpentry will be a very useful thing and, for the benefit of the service, may be reduced to a system. I have no doubt By's plan will be very good of its kind.' The model is still in the possession of the Royal Engineers.

By had plenty of work to do apart from making models. It was at Quebec, already the centre of an elaborate system of inland water transport, that he first became acquainted with canals. For all practical purposes it was the bateaux that carried Canada's burdens and the bateaux men were a race of skilled operators. So long as there was water enough to float them the bateaux were rowed or pulled; when there was not they were put on rollers and moved by what the Navy calls 'Armstrong's Patent', or muscle power. They came in two sizes, the older ones carrying about five tons and the newer Durham boats eight. The passage up-stream from Montreal to Kingston usually took about twelve days under oar and sail.

The importance of providing the water for circumventing rapids was plain to see and canals were already furnishng it wherever they could be made with the resources available on the spot. One of these was called the Cascades and on it By was set to work. There is little or no record surviving of the doings of an obscure subaltern at this time, but By was plainly much taken by the subject and acquired a lot of practical experience. One matter The Shop neither taught nor could have been expected to teach was how to enlist civilian labour, organise it, pay it or control it. This was difficult enough in England, as the early railway contractors were finding with their gangs of Irish. In Canada at that time it was harder still. Nevertheless it had to be done and it was done. His stint in Quebec gave By his initiation, but it was rudely interrupted. At the end of 1810 he was summoned back to join the Duke's army in Spain which was suffering a desperate shortage of military engineers. By had a hand in the second siege of Badajoz, an operation that demonstrated how much the British army had forgotten about siege-craft since Marlborough's day. Exactly what was By's part in the business is no longer known. Napier mentions three sapper officers by name but By is not one of them. Though Wellington by then was commanding a force of eight divisions he mustered barely thirty sapper officers and no rank and file at all until 1811. Even then the total strength of his Engineers was never more than about 100. In a private letter to Lord Liverpool, not included in his despatches and written after the third and successful siege, the Duke complained bitterly that the absence of proper Sapper element compelled him to launch an attack knowing full well that it would cost him many of his best infantry officers and men. Such sapper officers as there were, he asserted, did not turn their minds to the traditional operations; it was up to them to contrive practicable ways for the stormers to do their work without having to endure crippling losses and they were failing through lack of training and experience. Lord Liverpool rose to the occasion. Within weeks of Badajoz being finally taken six companies of sappers were under orders for Spain. On 4 August, 1812, the name of the Corps was changed to 'The Royal Sappers and Miners'.

John By did not remain in the Peninsula long enough to witness the Duke's only failure, the attack on Burgos. By that time he was home again, promoted to Major and in charge of the gunpowder factories at Faversham, Purfleet and Waltham Abbey. This unexciting task kept him in the service until 1821 when he was placed on the Unemployed List with the rank of Lieutenant-Colonel. The only record of By's time as the explosive expert consists of his model bridge. It was described in detail by the *Morning*

Chronicle of 14 February, 1816, and, as you may remember, Charles Pasley had a good opinion of it. By made the best he could of being an out-of-work officer with nothing but his half-pay. In 1818 he married the heiress of John March of Harley Street, the grandson of John Barker of Fairford Park in Gloucestershire. There is no reason to doubt that it was a love match; their lives together make that entirely plain. Nevertheless it was convenient that Mrs By was sufficiently well off to buy the estate of Shernfold Park at Frant, on the Kent and Sussex border. There for the next five years Colonel and Mrs By lived the life proper to a country gentleman and his wife. Enjoyable it must have been, but it may have grown stale rather quickly. The fact that he accepted the challenge to return to Canada and help with her defences against an un-neighbourly neighbour speaks for itself. The compliment being paid him after years of neglect was not to be refused. By, Mrs By and their daughters (the elder of whom was in due time to marry the son of Lord Ashburnham) overhauled their wardrobe with an eye to conditions even colder than those in Kent.

One invention had come about since By's last tour of duty and it was of first importance. The steam-driven paddle-tug could tow a bateau through narrow channels where none could have passed before. In spite of its tendency to blow up without warning, it was the steam tug that made the exploitation of Canada's great waterways practicable. His orders to build a canal some 130 miles long sounded a formidable undertaking but not an impossible one. The Grand Canal of China, dug out over a period of several centuries, was five times that length. In 1800 the Swedish engineer von Platen had built his famous staircase of eight deep locks running straight up a hillside. Pasley's friend Telford had designed the other Swedish masterpiece, the Trollhatten locks, which were already the subject of several books. Three centuries of experience lay behind the canal-builders of Bernadotte's kingdom. Behind By there was precious little; the Royal Staff Corps had produced the only known specimen. Mr Pitt's Royal Military Canal wanders some 20 miles across Romney Marsh without the need of locks; it had served its purpose for supplying Martello Towers but had no lessons for Colonel By. To construct something far bigger in a land of forest and swamp he would have to work by the light of nature, illuminated also by what he might remember of Professor Landsmann's teaching on the subject.

By the mid-1820s the revolutionary ardour at home seemed to have settled down and the distress brought about by a series of bad harvests was not nearly so widespread. Trade was at last beginning to restore itself and the Treasury had found a little money to spare. Canada was a long way off but it was an important source of timber for the navy, of wheat and of furs. At the back of many minds was a feeling that we had not behaved too well towards the Loyalists who had left their homes for the backwoods out of simple honest patriotism. America seemed to be thriving, for the 330-mile-long Erie Canal, linking New York City with the Great Lakes, was well under way — it was opened in 1825 — and the time seemed at last to have come when something had to be done to discourage any ideas of another invasion. De Witt Clinton's canal had been eight years in the building. It might be no more than a piece of development natural to an expanding nation but it would certainly be useful were any new War Hawks to come to power. It was time to look to Canada's own moat.

There was some limited experience of canal building among sappers past and present in the new world. Between 1779 and 1783 they had been at work on the Coteau du Lac and Cedars Canal: but these were comparatively small affairs built merely to by-pass rapids. There was a Royal Engineer establishment in Quebec which was known to be keen on the project. The CRE, Colonel Gother Mann, had been advocating canal-building for years averring that the tolls would cover construction costs. This seemed doubtful but capital investment ought eventually to pay off. During the war of 1812 much money had been spent on military transport between Quebec and Upper Canada. It had been calculated that it cost £200 to haul a single 24-pdr to its emplacement at Kingston. A canal seemed commercially a fair bet. The immediate question was who should build it.

The Duke — the Army knows only one Duke — was firm about it. 'Wherever the work can be done by contract, that mode should be preferred,' but the responsibility must lie at all times with the Engineers. 'It must happen that a number of settlers on a particular line of the proposed canal might be willing to work on the canal under the Engineers who would not choose to work under a contractor.' Very probably the Duke had in mind such places as Perth, a settlement founded in 1816 by discharged soldiers and settlers from Scotland. The Romans had employed veterans from their military settlements in Britain in exactly that way.

The Memorandum, dated June, 1826, ended with the opinion that the Governor-General and Chief Engineer ought to be kept as fully informed about everything, as were Colonels By and Wright, and 'should be requested to give those officers every assistance to enable them to carry into execution the instructions which they have received from the Board (of Ordnance)'. The Board should have the last word about everything, for it was the only military body the Duke trusted. Up to a point.

By, accompanied by his wife and daughters, presented himself at the office of Colonel Elias Durnford, CRE Quebec, on 30 May, 1826. He had been told before leaving home that £5,000 had been voted for the preliminary expenses and he had been assured by letter that whatever sums of money might be needed for the work itself would be furnished as a matter of course. Herein he was misled, but he cannot be blamed for not realising it. Politicians of a financial persuasion and practical soldiers make uneasy bedfellows. For a start, By was shown some plans and estimates prepared three years earlier by Samuel Clowes, a civil engineer employed by the Government of Upper Canada. His estimate, for locks of 11 feet only, was suspiciously low, a mere £69,783. So obviously suspect was it that Clowes had been ordered to try again; this time he was to calculate for locks of 15 feet, the same size as those being built for the Lachine Canal. The revised figure, still remarkably modest, was £145,000. By, understandably puzzled, deposited his family, moved on to Montreal and set out to canoe up the Ottawa River to the Chaudiere. It seemed important that he should find out certain things for himself.

The St Lawrence River had taken on a different aspect since he had last seen it, with the arrival of the steamers. By now they were commonplace, for it had been as long ago as 1809 when the first one had puffed its way from Montreal to Quebec. A look at Colonel By at 45 also may not come amiss, for he was no longer the stripling subaltern of his first tour. A portrait of him by an unknown artist, used as the basis of the statue, shows him as a large, burly man standing all of 6 feet in his riding boots and wearing an expression of unfailing good nature. This would be a necessary attribute, for Colonel By was to be a much humbugged man. Like all the Duke's officers he was carefully shaved except for a set of neatly trimmed mutton-chops. Indeed the head of John By on his statue looks much like the busts of the Emperor Vespasian. The next generation of notable sappers would be hairy men after the Victorian style but this indulgence would have been regarded by the Georgians as fit only for tramps and rabbit-trappers. The army disliked beards, save only for Pioneer Sergeants; a few decades later and there came the most famous paragraph in Queen's Regulations. 'The chin and under-lip will be shaved. The upper lip will not be shaved. Whiskers, if worn, will be of moderate length.' It lasted from the Crimea until after the Somme.

His reconnaissance finished, By arrived back at Montreal in August, 1826, and set up an office; there he transacted business with such people as were immediately available, including some of the contractors who had expressed an interest at working with him. These were the only men who could furnish the labour, skilled or otherwise, upon which the canal project would have to depend, for the army was in no position to take on the job by itself. By had asked for four companies of sappers to be sent; he had been given the answer that only two were available. The 15th Company Royal Sappers and Miners, arrived on 1 June, 1827, followed by the 7th in mid-September. His military force amounted to 162 men and nine officers. Though few in numbers, they included people trained in every kind of engineering skill and could both teach and supervise as necessary. The Montreal merchants welcomed the plan but had no particular interest in its military implications. Their concern was trade which, they asserted, would be better served by bringing the canal to the St Lawrence by way of Cornwall. By, on instructions, firmly squashed that. Kingston was to Canada what Dover was to England and no other route could be contemplated. The merchants reluctantly gave in. Even these preliminary discussions convinced By that Mr Clowes' estiamates were wildly optimistic. One of his first actions was to send a letter home in which he said flatly that the figure could not be less than £400,000. In September he set out with his three RE officers, Captain Bolton and Lieutenants Pooley and Crome, to see things for himself. The arrangement was that they should be met at the Ottawa end by the Governor-General, Lord Dalhousie, and should there make some firm decisions about the work to be done. The agreed rendezvous was a place called Wright's Village. the abode of one of the great Canadian patriarchs. Philemon Wright had arrived from Concord, Massachusetts, some 30 years earlier bringing with him, so it is said, a fortune of 30,000 dollars. When eventually he had decided upon the site of his new home he set to work with a will, clearing more than a thousand acres, furnishing himself with a herd of cattle and building a regular township complete with saw mill, grist mill and even, by the time By's party arrived, an hotel called The Columbia. There was a steam-boat service on the river, three churches, a well-stocked armoury (Wright was Colonel of his own militia), schools and wharves. After the long canoe journey it must have seemed like paradise. Wright was then about 70, and is described as being 6 feet tall and with a 'wonderfully strange, quick reflective and wild eye'. His village later took the name of Hull and is now part of the National Capital District. Dalhousie duly arrived and the party took counsel together.

The prospect before them looked as daunting as anything could be, for the land across which the canal would have to run had been untouched by man since the creation. Underneath much of it lay an expanse of the pre-Cambrian shield, among the most ancient rock formations known to geologists, well adapted to the growth of woods but inimical to any form of agriculture. That part of it between Kingston and Smith's Falls, known as the Frontenac Axis, was ancient rock undisturbed by anybody or anything since the last Ice Age had retreated, leaving behind it a desolation of lakes and hillocks. From the highest point of the Axis rose the headwaters of the Rideau and Cataraqui Rivers, the one running north-east to its confluence with the Ottawa, the other south-west until it poured into the lake at Kingston. The Rideau — so named by early voyageurs from the curtain-like apperance of the falls at the Ottawa end — ran through a plain of sandstone and limestone, the greater part of its length being made almost impassable by swamps and vegetation. The linking of the two river systems between Newboro Lake and the Upper Rideau, at the highest point of the Isthmus, looked like being the most difficult part of the entire work. By was gloomy about it, as well he might have been.

Soon after work had begun on digging and blasting the mile and a quarter of new waterway he wrote home that 'The oftener I examine the excavation now in progress the more I am convinced that it is going to be a more difficult piece than I had suspected'. Discoveries such as this — and there would be others — inevitably added much to the cost. Those concerned with the matter in London seemed unreceptive to the idea that such things must happen in an unmapped waste land.

A second and invisible menace hung around the swamps. Young gentlemen at The Shop had been taught how to drain morasses; their instructors had been silent on the subject of swamp fever. Malaria, as its name suggests, was reckoned to be the result of breathing bad air — Buenos Aires was so named to mark its freedom from such things — and there was nothing to be done about it. This seems hard to explain. As long ago as 1683 the wife of the Governor of Peru had been cured by an infusion of cinchona bark, variously called Jesuit's bark or quinine. An impure form of the prophylactic had been made by Gomez at Lisbon in 1810 and by 1820 the alkaloid had been isolated. Quinine had entered the pharmacopoeia long before the Rideau Canal was begun but it still attracted little interest. The price probably had something to do with it and the criminality of the anopheles mosquito was still unsuspected. In most parts of the world, and for a long time to come, malaria was accepted like the common cold. Either you got it or you did not. If you did, you would be lucky to recover; even if you did get over it, the debilitating effect would not be quickly shaken off. By had two serious bouts; the second one was nearly fatal.

The senior of his task-masters at this time was Lord Dalhousie, Governor-in-Chief of British North America. Dalhousie knew exactly what he wanted and had made some preparations. The canal, of course, was the first priority, but it was not to be everything. There was also to be a fine city. Three years earlier, and looking forward to the day when it would take shape, he had bought a large parcel of land between the Chaudiere Falls and the Rideau River from a Mr Fraser. He had paid 750 dollars; from Fraser's point of view it was not a bad bargain. He had bought it from one of the original United Empire Loyalists for $12. By was ordered to have it properly surveyed and to set aside as building lots everything that would not be wanted for the canal. This was the state of affairs in September, 1826, when Dalhousie and By stood on Philemon Wright's wharf and tried to see in their minds where the Entrance Locks would go. Their eyes revealed only row upon row of forest trees. The work would not be made easier by staring at it; they discussed the details of what must be done and settled on the cleft where the canal should start. Wright, an enthusiast for the whole scheme, was able to help by finding labour among his own people. By caused advertisements to be placed in the *Montreal Herald* under the heading 'SPREADING THE NEWS ABOUT BYTOWN'. This was the first time the name appeared in print. The building lots were advertised and the labourers hired. Next came the building of the bridge across the Ottawa River, something that had to be done before Dalhousie's city could be even contemplated.

They wasted no time, for Dalhousie himself laid the cornerstone of the first span on 28 September. The ceremony is said to have included Masonic honours — there were plenty of masons about — and a selection of coins was interred. Much of the bridge work was handed over to John McTaggart, a civilian who had been sent out from Scotland as Clerk of Works and who was to remain on the job for the next three years. Mention must also be made of another of the assistant engineers named Thomas Burrowes. His contribution to the construction work does not seem to have been outstanding but he alone has left an enduring memorial. Mr Burrowes was also an artist. He had, it is said, been trained as a draughtsman of the Board of Ordnance at the establishment known as the Drawing Room in the Tower of London where there was a notable school of painters founded half a century earlier by Paul Sandby, sometimes called 'the father of English watercolour art'. Captious critics have been heard to say that Mr Burrowes was not so much a Jan Vermeer of Delft as a Grandma Moses, but his watercolours were the nearest thing then possible to a photographic record of the progress of By's work. They are an essential study for those seeking a good understanding of what happened.

The bridge was to have eight spans in all, five of 60 feet each, two of 70 with another 200 feet over the gap known as La Grande Chaudiere. By put the first rope across it by a variation on the method well known to the Black Prince's archers. A cord was fixed to a grapnel and fired across from a small gun. Whether or not this was a technique taught at The Shop is not now remembered. The contractor in charge of the masonry, Thomas McKay, was an experienced hand fresh from the Lachine canal but even he could not compete with a Canadian winter. Regularly every morning snow had to be swept from the masons' platform, a watch had to be kept for floating ice and on several days the mercury froze in the thermometers. This, however, was a hard generation and only one man suffered frostbite. It is unsurprising to be told that building the bridge took a long time. A temporary affair, swung on ropes over the gap, was in existence at the end of the first year – Lord and Lady Dalhousie crossed it on 26 September, 1827 – but it was not until March, 1828, that the work was finished. Before any celebration could take place a block of floating ice wrecked the scow supporting the middle of the long span and it collapsed. Another year's work was needed to make good the damage. Even then the structure lasted only until 1835; after this second collapse it was replaced by a suspension bridge.

A smaller bridge, built by the Sappers themselves in 1830, spanned the canal and furnished a link between what were known as Upper and Lower Bytown. Though less spectacular than MacTaggart's Union Bridge, it was solider. In 1912, when reconstruction of the city centre made its removal necessary, Sappers Bridge defied the dynamite. It took three hours of bombing by a 2-ton boulder dropped from a height of 50 feet before it gave way. The Corps builds to last.

By returned to Montreal leaving MacTaggart to oversee the laying-out of the first buildings and the clearance of bush on both sides of the valley where the Entrance Locks would go. Barracks and hospitals went up to replace the tents and a house was put up for the Colonel. It was given a verandah which, according to one visitor, commanded 'the most magnificent view that the splendid scenery of Canada affords'. The house was constructed from small boulders bonded together and thickly plastered with mud and clay; this worked very satisfactorily and the By family lived in comfort.

John By was nothing like a permanent resident there. From his office in Montreal he was more fully occupied, partly in work of diplomacy. Tentative plans for the canal, prepared in London, looked well enough there, but were now realized to be not practical. The difficulty was that many of them had been either proposed or approved by the Duke himself. He had never set foot in Canada, but that was not sufficient reason to criticize him. The Duke possessed a stronger common sense than most men and never talked nonsense. His original idea, propounded in 1819, had been for a canal running from Kingston to a point on Georgian Bay due north of where Toronto now stands and using existing lakes and rivers for communication with the interior. This was a purely military measure, designed to make sure that the Navy could use its ships on any of the Great Lakes in a future war. It could have no other purpose and was quietly dropped. The Duke was not pleased. It had also become evident quite early on that his other proposed route by Irish Lake (or Creek as he called it) was also unsatisfactory, although it had more supporters than the first. John MacTaggart, squelching, crashing and paddling through bush and swamp, was finding a better way while By was left to deal with the paper work, mainly dealing with plans, negotiating with landowners and settling terms with the contractors.

The original idea of having a waterway provided largely by nature, using the Rideau and Cataraqui Rivers and their attendant lakes with only a small amount of canal digging, had quickly to be discarded. The route was, beyond argument, the best to be had, but the builders would have to resign themselves to a lot of hard work on it. In addition to the eight locks at the Ottawa end, raising the vessels using them by 82 feet, there would be many more needed along the course of the canal. In the end they totalled thirty-nine, along with twenty-four dams and eighteen miles of dug-out artificial watercourses. Each piece of work demanded a contractor for the masonry and labourers for the navvying. The office work for all this kept By at his desk throughout the last months of 1826 and the greater part of 1827. Though not everybody enjoys a Canadian winter its conditions made MacTaggart's task possible. A man cannot walk over mud accumulated during thousands of years and arteried with clinging vegetation. Once it has frozen hard the thing becomes possible. MacTaggart pressed on.

As might have been foreseen in a project of such size, there was criticism both of the plans and of By personally. In a letter written from his home in Reigate on 30 October, 1827, a bare month after the Dalhousies had made their crossing of the Union Bridge, Sir James Carmichael Smyth had something to say to the Duke. The men were old friends. Smyth, a sapper, had been one of the small party (Pasley was another) that had accompanied Wellington to the Low Countries in July, 1814. A full year before Waterloo was fought and long before anyone else even considered the possibility of a resurgent Bonaparte, the Duke was looking ahead and planning for every possible contingency. James Carmichael Smyth had been his cartographer and produced beautiful maps of the last campaign many months before it was fought. During the course of it he had been the Duke's CRE. Now he was Chairman of the Committee sent to Canada to inspect what By was doing and report on it. Parts of what he had seen appeared excellent.

'Whatever may have been Colonel By's original errors, he is certainly now getting on with very great zeal and activity.' That was enough of compliments. Sir James wrote on. 'He certainly at first wrote home a great deal of nonsense, and formed the most unmilitary notions as to the defence of Canada, proposing to remove the Richelieu Rapids, and other obstacles, on which the safety of the province in a great measure depends. His estimate for £1,200,000 was also very ridiculous. He has also, perhaps, been unguarded in his conversation in allowing these notions of his to become public.' It was time for a kind word. 'With all this, he appears however to deserve the character they entertain of him at General Mann's office of being a very active and capable officer, and well qualified to execute the details of his work. I should hope your Grace will have no further cause of uneasiness or reference; and that in the year 1830 this most useful work, as connected with the permanent security of Canada will be entirely completed.' Sir James then expressed the hope that Canadian boatmen would use the canal 'as it ought to be cheaper than paying the very heavy charges for pilotage through St Lawrence rapids'.

By was a colonel of engineers and not a captain of industry. To him it seemed obvious that his duty was to get on with the job rather than watch people hanging uselessly about while Parliament voted money and the seasons changed. He had one early experience of contractors that may have furnished a lesson. Mr Fenelon, who will appear again, had been unable to find the shovels and wheelbarrows he had contracted to provide and announced that the deal was off. In an effort to prevent this sort of thing happening again By caused a statement to be published in the Montreal newspapers. No contractor was wanted unless 'he is a practical artist, competent for what he professes'. The nature of the tasks to be undertaken was explained. 'The works of the Rideau Canal seem to divide themselves into the following great branches; building and finishing locks of heavy masonry, excavating earth and clay, excavating rock and gravel, constructing heavy dams across the rideau of rough rubble masonry, framing aqueducts and bridges of wood etc.' As some sort of reassurance, he informed aspirants that a subaltern's command of sixty soldiers would always be stationed near each contract work, that surgeons would be engaged and furnished with all necessary medicines, and that plenty of spirits and provisions of all kinds with camp equipment would be supplied by the Government. Thus encouraged, the contractors formed up to By's office.

The parties to the contracts into which they entered were the Commissary-General to His Majesty's Forces in Canada on the one hand and a loose consortium on the other. Four contractors were involved; Thomas McKay, John Redpath, Robert Drummond and the firm of Phillips and White. Scottish-sounding names all of them, and canny men with particular skill in masonry. As between themselves they agreed to pool all profits and share losses. It was a sensible arrangement and seems to have worked a rough justice.

Another of By's labours was to seek out the ownership of land and acquire it. One might have imagined that parcels of ancient chaos, practically unvisited by white men, would have belonged to nobody in particular. One would have been wrong. Every square inch seemed to have an owner, even if his title was debatable. In days before compulsory purchase was even thinkable each claim had to be settled, and settled quickly. The idea of paying money for something like Cranberry Lake or Dow's Great Swamp seems odd but there was no avoiding it and it was a sellers' market. Though it had not been any part of his education so far, Colonel By managed. The land became Government land.

The provision of labour was a fairly simple business, by courtesy of Napoleon Bonaparte. In consequence of his economic sanctions against England the Royal Navy had been deprived of its usual sources of timber in Scandinavia. This meant a vast increase in the trade with North America and the shipowners had cast around to find something to carry on the outward voyage. They found it in the shape of Irish emigrants. Ireland had known potato famines long before 1840 and there was no shortage of applicants for passages at the very low fares then offered. It was possible to get a berth to Quebec for 2 or 3 pounds. No Catholic Irishman, of course, wanted to remain in a country under the flag he hated but once in Quebec it was no great matter to move on another 180 miles to Montreal and then to cross into the United States on foot. The new arrivals were inevitably destitute, diseased and of little skill at anything but they were there and would gladly work for wages. Of the 3,000 or so men employed on the canal once the contractors had got into the swing of things a large proportion had been provided by the Limerick ship-owners. Much the same thing was soon to happen in England when the railways came to be built. The Irish, with their families, seemed able to live like the birds and beasts. Proper feeding and regular work soon made new men of them but their casualties from fecklessness were incessant. There was, as in England, another side to it. A sergeant and a dozen sappers who might have been more usefully employed elsewhere had to be kept as a permanent guard over the liquor stores at Bytown: more than once they had to take up arms to put down riots amongst drink-maddened men. When the canal was completed most of the Irish disappeared overnight, presumably off to Philadelphia - more probably Buffalo - in the morning. Some stayed in the valley of the Ottawa but many of them had already gone on a longer journey. The Canadian winter and the Cranberry Marsh bugs saw to that, assisted by over-indulgence in the liquor they brewed for themselves and which was charitably called whisky.

Apart from the Irish, the contractors' labour force was drawn more or less equally from the English- and French-speaking inhabitants. Though they mixed hardly at all and had little love for each other they seem to have got along well enough. One contribution made by the French was of a kind peculiar to themselves. The voyageurs, engaged normally in the fur trade, were a race apart and John By both liked and admired them. The big canots-de-maitres, 36 feet long and made from the traditional birch bark, were the only form of water transport that could be used throughout the Rideau and Cataraqui systems; the suitability of their design and the skill of their paddlers made them capable of incredible feats. When By made his first voyage of discovery he hired six of them and was carried the entire length of the course in three days. He had expected it to take much longer. Such was the reputation of the voyageurs that Sir Garnet Wolseley, with memories of his Red River expedition in 1870, recruited a corps of them in 1884 for the relief of General Gordon — another sapper — in Khartoum. It was not as easy as it sounded, for railways had taken away the occupation of the best of them. Few of those who went would have been called voyageurs by their fathers: most were lumberjacks, while others were bank clerks or working in insurance. For all that, they got his whale-boats up the Nile better than anybody else might have done.

As the same time as By was working on plans and contracts, some of his young officers were walking the course along with John MacTaggart. It was from their detailed examination of the difficulties to be surmounted and the report they drew up that By made his decision on the final line the canal would take.

From the point where the Rideau Falls splash into the Ottawa River to the Hog's Back rapids was something like five miles. Both banks consisted of glutinous mud surmounted by bush, conditions that made them impassable to any man on foot. The party had no choice but to wait for it to freeze. As a result it took them five days, including Christmas Day, 1826, to struggle as far as Dow's Great Swamp. Next came the first set of rapids, six or seven miles of them, as far as Long Island; there, after a short reach of stillwater, they began again, dropping 24 feet in the next four miles. The twenty that they had to cover after Long Island were better, though still with thick forest on both banks; by the time the next series of rapids, Burritt's, Nicholson's and Merrick's Mill, were reached some signs began to suggest that the human race still existed. At the last settlement lived James Clowes, an enterprising man who had started up a limestone quarry. He was also the connecting-file with civilization, for his home was the cross-roads. Here came in the track from Prescott, 20-odd miles to the south east, which made its way over Mr Merrick's bridge until it reached Perth, another 30 miles to the north-west. For a time, after leaving Mr Clowes, the surveyors had easier going, through little settlements cleared from the woods by pioneers whose names still belong to them. After the next eight miles, however, the clearings ceased at Maitlands and the banks once more became low and swampy. After passing Old Sly's house the river began another of its downhill rushes, racing through a channel 50 feet wide and dropping 35 feet in a couple of furlongs. In what was to become the town of Smith's Falls the only sign of life was a little saw-mill. Then followed five more miles of rapids until the river merged into the 23-mile long Rideau Lake. Once the Lake and its two narrows had been traversed, the watershed was reached and the canoes had to be carried a mile and half to the next.

Between the aptly named Mud Lake and Clear Lake the explorers stood on an isthmus, usually called 'the height of land'. They had travelled 90 miles along the Rideau and might reasonably have supposed that, with only 30 miles of the Cataraqui to go, the worst was over. If so, they were wrong. At its beginning the new river promised a pleasant journey, wandering through the Indian and Sand Lakes until they came to Chaffey's Mills. There they found some of the comforts of civilization. A right-minded settler had established not merely a saw-mill but a small distillery. Fortified by its product and having negotiated Mosquito Lake by way of a fall, a dam and a rocky channel that dropped 60 feet in less than a mile, they found themselves inside one of the worst obstacles of all. Cranberry Lake, with its faint echo of Thanksgiving and all that went with it, sounded as if it should be quite an agreeable place. It proved, in fact, one of the most disagreeable in the entire system. The topography was bad enough, 18 miles by 2 of solid cranberry bushes which appeared to have been established since the Creation; so firmly established indeed that the bushes floated on the surface of the water connected to a marvellous and impenetrable system of roots anchoring them to the lake bed. A tiny channel, just passable to a canoe, led to Round Tail Falls where the Cataraqui River began its descent to Kingston but everywhere else there was solid vegetation. If this were not enough, the lake sustained a vigorous insect life and a remarkable stench. Sappers, by virtue of their occupation, were authorities on the bugs of all nations but nobody had previously come across them in such profusion or so well-organized. There were black flies and the invisible tormentors called by the Indians 'no see ums' by day; malaria-carrying mosquitoes took over for the night shifts. Every one of them knew its business and passed up no opportunity for bite or sting.

MacTaggart, justly, called it 'this infernal place' and denied it the name of the lake. To him it was always 'Cranberry Swamp'. It reeked of fever — 'miasma' was the word currently in use — and it was to cause the construction gangs far more difficulty than any other reach. Once the mosquitoes had got you, you put up with the three days of shivering, sweating, violent headaches, delirium and the feeling that the eyes were embedded in red-hot sand. Then, if you were lucky, the fever ran its course, leaving only a deathly weakness for a long time to come. Cranberry Lake exacted a heavy toll from those who intruded upon its ancient peace. Soon after Cranberry Lake came what Bonnycastle reckoned 'a most gloomy spot conducing to suicide, Brewer's Mills'.

Like everything else, the journey had an end. Once Round Tail was left behind there remained only about 20 more miles to Kingston and the presence of man was becoming more and more apparent. Mills, a word that crops up frequently in the names of Canadian towns, appeared from time to time, the last being the big saw-mill built by the government some years before to provide the dockyard with timber. By then the end was almost in sight. After a sharp drop of 26 feet into Cataraqui Bay there was an easy channel leading them into the town.

MacTaggart and the sapper officers promptly sat down and drew up a detailed report for By in Montreal. It spoke of falls and rapids that would have to be dammed and controlled, of locks to be built and of channels to be dug out in order to circumvent swamps and portages. All of it would have to be done by the old means, using only pick, shovel, wheelbarrow, block and tackle, axe, saw and muscle. Steam power, for now, was useful only in the tugboats. By was not unduly troubled by the findings. His own sappers could provide expertise, the contractors and labourers would do their share and the pre-Cambrian Shield could at least be made to yield up all they needed in the way of rock and timber.

The first priority had to be the Entrance Locks. By and his family took up residence at their house overlooking the work and entertained there a flow of visitors. Sir John Franklin, later to be lost with his two ships and their crews in the Arctic ice, turned up unexpectedly in August, 1827. He had just finished a three-year stint exploring the Mackenzie River with a party of French voyageurs. Mary Durnford, daughter of Lieutenant-General Elias

Durnford RE, wrote in her *Family Recollections* that 'Colonel By enjoyed from his wife a handsome private income, and his showy hospitable mode of living made him universally popular and beloved'.

Although Franklin was only passing through By persuaded him to lay the first stone of Lock No 3. Next to visit the scene were the Dalhousies, their time as Governor and wife nearly up. On the exact anniversary of the first visit during which he and By settled on the site for the Entrance Locks, 26 September, the Earl and Countess landed at Hull. Three days later he marked the occasion by laying the corner-stone on the east side of the canal; a 2-ton chunk of ancient rock had been shaped and made ready by masons whose 'practical artistry' could hardly have been questioned. A noble party with much rum followed.

It quickly became a point of honour for any grandee, Canadian or visitor, who happened to be about the place to pay a call on the Bys and several accounts survive of the pleasant home and warm hospitality. Esther By's share in building the Rideau Canal was by no means negligible. Archdeacon Strachan was pleased to find a Methodist chapel but regretted that no proper Anglican church had been built. It should not have surprised him all that much. Methodism had been a powerful force in the Duke's army in Spain and he had always been a friend to it. The fact that the Wesleys and Wellesleys were related was incidental. The reason was, as the Duke regularly complained, that the Church would persist in sending him chaplains of such poor quality.

Mrs By does not appear often in the records but there is one glimpse of her that survives. Mrs Simpson, whose husband George worked for the Hudson's Bay Company, put it in her diary. 'We were kindly received by Mrs By, a very agreeable and accomplished young woman who insisted upon us stopping to breakfast with her.' Like the other callers Mrs Simpson was greatly taken by the view from the verandah, 'overlooking one of the most beautiful spots I have seen in this country'.

Canada being what it was, there was no shortage of trained carpenters who could do anything with wood. Masons were another matter. Plenty of them were available but because of their origins in lowland Scotland and Ulster they were accustomed only to working in dry-stone. The technique serves well enough above the water level but it does not lend itself to the building of dams. For this ashlar blocks firmly cemented together are essential and cement of hydraulic quality was both scarce and dear. For once the builders had a stroke of good fortune, helped out by local knowledge. The Wright family led them to a spot on the opposite bank of the Ottawa where a small quarry existed of a rock which when burnt and ground fine produced cement of far better quality than anything that was being imported. From these small beginnings grew up the present day works of the Canada Cement Company. The new product, forced into the interstices through tin tubes, proved highly successful and bonded the great staircase of the Entrance Locks into something as firm as the Pyramids. After that it became an essential ingredient of most of the locks and dams throughout the system.

As nothing could be made of Dow's Great Swamp the only possible course was to by-pass it. This was effected by means of a long embankment which, when complete, flooded the place into what became Dow's Lake. The Entrance Locks were connected to the Hog's Back by an artificial channel, its level carefully maintained above that of the Rideau River.

By needed no reminding that he would be called upon to render a strict account of every penny spent; accordingly, during 1827, he sent Lieut. Pooley back to London with the latest estimate of £474,000. The Committee of Engineers Officers under Sir Archibald Bryce sat in the old War Office building in Pall Mall — since 1907 it has been the Royal Automobile Club — and went carefully through the figures. They were not entirely happy about them since they based their calculations on the cost of locks bigger than those the Committee had bargained for. This was, for By, an article of faith. In order to ascertain how much more expensive the larger size (of 134 feet by 34) would make the cost the Committee decided to make its own assessment on the spot. Two senior RE officers, Colonels Fanshawe and Lewis, were sent out in the following year. The business ended with the Committee agreeing that By had been right all along but it justified its existence by scaling the plans down a little below By's recommended size.

Though his accounts were models of what such things should be, John By seems to have had the impression that he had been given the green light to set the entire scheme in motion. The contractors were put to work at both the Ottawa and Kingston ends and the tricky part, the Isthmus by Newboro', was started soon afterwards.

It hardly seems necessary for a book such as this to give a detailed account of every piece of work done. It is all set out in that wonderful repository of all engineering lore, the Professional Papers of the Royal Engineers. The relevant articles are all by Sapper officers, none of them above the rank of Lieutenant, and they were written for the edification of other Sappers. As the authors were young men with their careers in front of them, and well aware that their readers would include the heads of their Corps, they wrote nothing but hard professional exegeses of what they had seen and done. Professional papers eschew lightness of touch and a working knowledge of engineering is needed to wring out every drop of the information they give. Lieutenants — both were to rise far higher — Frome and Denison have left a worthy legacy for those who come after them. They can be scathing when they wish. For example, the collapses of MacTaggart's Union Bridge are bluntly ascribed to 'weak and faulty abutments'. Sappers may quite fairly criticise civilian contractors.

The outstanding pieces of work on the system were four in number, the Hog's Back Dam near Bytown, Smith's Falls at about the halfway mark, Jones' Falls on the Kingston side of the Isthmus where the water from Sand Lake drops 60 feet into the Cranberry Swamp through a rocky gorge with steep banks sometimes 90 feet high, and the complex dam and lock arrangements at Kingston Mills. By's plan for dealing with rapids was largely of his own devising, though something of the same kind had been carried out on a smaller scale in the United States. High dams would be built to flood the rapids out, thus creating what was called a stillwater system upstream. The ideal was eventually proved sound, but only after much trial and error.

Building the eight Entrance Locks provided no more difficulty than might reasonably have been expected. The excavating was done by a contractor named Pennyfeather, who disappeared from the scene as soon as he had made his contribution. Very possibly he was one of those men, better with a pick than a pen, to whom the canal was a financial disaster. The masonry was the work of a man whose skill is remembered in the Public Archives and proclaimed by the locks themselves. Thomas McKay's is a memorable name in Canada. Like the Sappers, he built for eternity. The locks, each made from the hard local stone upon inverted arches, were held together where necessary by iron straps and grouted with the Wright cement in the fashion already described. Two famous soldiers came to inspect his work and had complimentary things to say about it. Both were men whose compliments were worth having. Sir James Kempt, after Maida and a distinguished career in the Peninsula including the final storming of Badajoz, had been one of the Duke's most trusted subordinates at Waterloo. When Sir Thomas Picton fell, it was upon Kempt that command of the 5th Division devolved and it was his column, reduced to a fraction of its size at the beginning, which charged Bonaparte's Young Guard and routed it. He was one of the army's best-liked Generals. Harry Smith, not a man given to over-praise, calls him 'my dear friend'. The other, as Lieut.-Colonel John Colborne of the 52nd, had been the best CO of the best battalion in the Duke's army and was the man who, again at Waterloo, had seized the moment when the Imperial Guard looked like wavering and broke it into a panicky rabble. Kempt was now about to take office as Administrator of the Government of Canada. Both men were on terms of friendship with the Duke and were useful allies to that other Peninsular veteran, John By. The British Army gave Canada of its best.

The Hog's Back Dam was a more difficult business than the Entrance Locks. Fortunately for history one of the sapper officers working on it, Lieut. Denison, has preserved the record by setting down his experiences in an article published in the Professional Papers. He tells how the original contract was given to Mr Fenlon (who appears elsewhere as Fenelon) whom we have already met. By may have been too trusting in his dealings with this expert for Fenlon's price for the job was surprisingly low, a little over £4,500 as against an estimate of nearly £11,000. Denison is scornful. 'Mr. Fenlon, having made what he conceived to be the necessary preparations for the work, commenced his operations on the right bank of the river in the summer of 1827, as soon as the spring floods had subsided. He threw stones, earth and rubbish into the bed of the river, so as to form a sort of *jetée,* by which the channel was contracted to about half of its original width, and behind this mass he built his key-work to the height of 37 feet. Having accomplished so much of his plan, he attempted in the autumn to close up the unfinished portion. He cut a small channel through the rock on the right hand bank of the river, close to the flank of the dam; the bottom of this channel was about 27 feet above the bed of the river, and its purpose was to serve as a waste-weir to carry off the water when raised to that height. Having taken this precaution he attempted to close the opening by throwing in stones, rubbish, etc and had succeeded in raising the water nearly high enough to flow through his waste-weir, when a sudden flood in the river swept away all the unfinished portion of his work, leaving it in much the same state as it was in the summer before the attempt to complete it had been made.' Exit Mr Fenlon. Enter the Royal Engineers after the Welland Canal contractors had refused to touch the job. Seven Sapper officers, of whom Denison was one, were bidden to start the work all over again. By 1 April, 1828, they had managed to erect a rough wooden dam but it lacked the strength to stand up to another flood and was swept away in its turn. The following year and a half were taken up, during such parts of it as the weather allowed, by trying yet again, this time with the assistance of 'a Mr Wright'. By November, 1829, all looked as if the task was near to a successful end. A 'sort of coffer-dam or caisson, made of rough timber notched together and pinned at the angles' had been fixed across the opening of the dam, the whole thing greatly strengthened and a door made of oak logs set in place to close the opening thus diverting the water down a waste channel. As winter closed in work began on making the key-work behind it. So intense was the frost that earth for fillings could only be got by blasting. By March, 1830, the key-work had reached a height of 37 feet with the earth and clay in front rising up to 50 feet. By the end of the month everything appeared satisfactory, the main body of the dam was nearly watertight and it showed no signs of settling. Then, once more on All Fools' Day, the water began to rise. Two days later most of the work carried out with such effort had for the second time been swept away and most of it was to be done yet again.

Denison makes one point that is worth remembering. 'The enormous power of the frost in Canada was exemplified in an extraordinary way during this catastrophe: the whole mass of earth

above the level of the water remaining suspended for about 5 minutes after the key-work had given way, forming an arch of at least
50 foot span, under which the river roared and foamed, and over
which several people passed safely: in a short time, however, the
action of the water, widening the breach, carried away the abutments of this arch, and the whole was precipitated into the river.'

Like Bruce and his spider, the Sappers set to work again. The
original plan of wedging rough blocks of locally quarried stone into
a mass so compact that it would stand up to the pressure now
known to be waiting for it was given up. When the final attempt
began in July it took the form of massive timber frames pushed
out from the banks, guyed against the current, with each bay being
loaded with stone enabling it to resist the action of the water. Once
the frame had reached the required height a roadway was formed
along the top and the bays at the ends filled in with small stones
and gravel. Large blocks were lowered into place at the rear and
the front was filled in with clay and more gravel. In this fashion
was formed a mass with its base extending some 300 feet upriver.
'Every expedient which the skill of the officer in charge of the
work could devise, or the means at his disposal enable him to
execute, was put in practice to guarantee the work against accidents
or failures,' Denison wrote. They were sufficient.

By had, of necessity, been much caught up in the Hog's Back
failures and spent a good part of the year 1829 — apart from a spell
of illness — on the spot. The final plan was his own, made in
conjunction with Philemon Wright (the 'a Mr Wright' referred to
by Denison) and Captain Victor, the senior Sapper officer present.
With the Hog's Back Dam nearly finished, Dow's Great Swamp
tamed by a mighty earthwork and the canal excavated by the
navvies — an unaffectionate diminutive of 'inland navigators' —
from the Entrance Locks to the dam a decent start had been made
at the Ottawa River end. South of Hog's Back the canal merges
into the Rideau River itself. It hardly seems necessary to give a
detailed account of all that was done over the 120 miles or so that
separated the confluence from the terminus at Kingston. There
are, however, some works that cannot be omitted. Among all the
Indian and French names of rivers and other geographical features
two homely ones stand out. At the ends of the middle third of the
canal lay falls named Smith and Jones. Smith, it seems, is a

misspelling of the surname of the Loyalist settler, Major Smyth. Charles Jones was the then owner of much land on the canal site. Neither has any great history, but their memorials should be as permanent as Canada itself.

By handed over the construction of the dam and locks designed for the circumvention of Smith's Falls to his trusted subordinate Lieutenant Pooley on his return from London. Very probably it was a relief to him after haggling over figures with the Committee. By had had to do some haggling on his own account, for the owner of the land upon which the dam and lock flight were to go had large ideas on its value. Mr Ward demanded £5,000. Eventually he settled for £1,500. Smith's Falls looked at first sight more of a problem than they proved. The river dropped 36 feet in a couple of furlongs but nature had for once provided a suitable depression in the rock that lent itself to lock-building. By was fortunate in his contractor, a young Ulsterman named Simpson who had had some canal experience in the United States. Both men knew their business perfectly. Simpson might have been expected to, for it was his trade. As for Pooley, one never ceases to marvel at the skill and organizing ability of young men of the lowest commissioned rank in carrying out work that would in more recent times demand teams of experts of one kind and another. Work went on at Smith's Falls without any of the setbacks that had afflicted the Hog's Back construction. The main obstacles were springs which proliferated everywhere and bugs that did the same. MacTaggart, who ought to have known, claims that the place was infested by hornets that stung the surveyors painfully as they set about their work. The back-breaking labour of blasting, drilling by hand in rock like marble and its removal by wheelbarrow went pretty much according to plan. By could safely leave the dam and three locks to the care of his men on the spot.

Jones Falls was quite another matter, and the building of a 350-foot dam along with a flight of four locks is reckoned to be By's masterpiece. The credit has to be shared with the contractor who was probably the best of the chosen few. The name of Simpson is all but forgotten: that of John Redpath remains famous in Canada as it deserves to be. Barrowload by barrowload his men painstakingly built up a clay dam behind which the masons set to work upon putting in place their blocks of stone. About 200 men, forty of them skilled masons, were kept labouring all the time at extracting and shaping stone from nearby quarries and hauling it by oxen to the river. There, using little hand-cranes, they shifted it on to the scows that carried the cut ashlar, each piece 6 feet by 4 by 18 inches, to the places where it was needed. It was fortunate that the Canadian lepidoptera does not include the tsetse fly, for animal transport was essential. By, on his great black horse, was a familiar feature of the landscape. Accidents apart, the worst enemy during summer was malaria; at one point in 1828 the entire company, doctors included, were struck down and a graveyard had to be set up near the dam. Nevertheless the work went on, even if sometimes by fits and starts. By the time the great arch dam was finished, carried out almost entirely in dry stone, it was the highest thing of its kind on the American continent. On a radius of 245 feet between solid rock walls and with a base narrowing from 27½ feet to 21½ it stood — and still stands — 62 feet high. The clay and earth dam on the upstream side runs at the bottom some 127 feet out under the water. One must be wary of adjectives but for such a work carried out in a remote wilderness with no source of power but that of man and beast a superlative can surely be justified. The labour was local Scots and French Canadian but the brain was nurtured in The Shop.

Last, and worst, was MacTaggart's Cranberry Swamp. Here, of course, the difficulties were of an entirely different kind. It was a great overgrown, fever-ridden morass in which even By, an intrepid and skilful canoe hand, had once been lost and only by good fortune avoided death in its nastiest form.

The making of great earthworks demanded many hands to ply shovel and barrow until a sufficient height had been achieved and many of the labourers were Irish. Though willing enough, they proved extremely vulnerable and they sickened and died in numbers unrecorded. By did his best for them but both nature and red tape were against him. The navvies, though well-paid for their efforts, refused to buy the blankets provided at low prices and many died from cold. MacTaggart says that sulphate of quinine was prescribed by the doctors but it was so dear that few could afford it. In any event, quinine taken after malaria has struck is not an infallible cure: only by taking the daily dose of five grains as a prophylactic can a man hope to escape the vengeance of the anopheles mosquito and this does not seem to have been understood at the time. Not that it would have made much difference. Soldiers have always hated taking the stuff, largely because of its disagreeable taste, and the Irish would have been no better. And it is unlikely that there would have been enough to go round in any case. By himself suffered a very severe attack and for a time was not expected to live. Only a tough constitution, a fierce determination and the devoted nursing of Esther By carried him through. MacTaggart fared worse and had to be sent home. The records show that, on the insistence of Sir James Kempt and in spite of By's attempts to save him, he was sacked for drunkenness. It is a pity that we no longer know how this came about. Kempt was not a peppery man: it may be that MacTaggart held a civilian view of all Generals and expressed it too vehemently. Certainly he bore no malice against By, for he appeared before the Commission, of which more later, and stoutly defended his actions. His occupation gone, John MacTaggart went home and wrote his book *Three Years In Canada*.

The two doctors, Tuthill and Robinson, were responsible for the whole length of the canal and travelled their rounds on horseback. When the last named, who was based on the Isthmus, asked for extra forage By was obliged to pass on the request to Colonel Durnford at Quebec who had in turn to seek approval from the Inspector-General of Hospitals. Mr Routh of the Commissary-General's office seems to have gone out of his way to make matters as difficult as possible. Every indent for the smallest thing had to be submitted in triplicate for approval and six individuals were needed to put their signatures to it before any stores could be issued. The contractors were paid in cash at Montreal, the money for wages being sent on by canoe. When By asked that they be paid by cheque at Kingston he was turned down flat.

In spite of all these vicissitudes the work went on and by mid-1831 most of the canal along the Rideau River was in fairly regular use. The Isthmus was still the worst part of it and it became necessary to send 15 Company RS&M from Bytown to work there under Captain Cole. Eighty-one men, assuming the company to have been at full strength, cannot have made all that much difference. It seems fair to assume that they supervised the labourers rather than acted as navvies themselves. Lieutenant Briscoe was put in charge at Kingston Mills, another 'drowning out' operation, and after a while By decided that it would be better to give his officers wider responsibilities. From about autumn 1829 each was given a stretch of waterway containing three or four locks and had, so far as was possible, to inspect progress on each one daily. Among their number was Lieutenant Frome whose essay on the subject is in the Professional Papers, under the date 28 February, 1837. The military nature of the whole business was underlined by the building of block-houses at all vulnerable points.

The end came, fortuitously, on 24 May, 1832, the 13th birthday of the future Queen Victoria and for many years celebrated as Empire Day. The little steamer *Pumper* — her normal function was to pump out water from coffer dams — began to thrash her paddles at about noon and John By, suitably attended, embarked on the passage from Kingston to the town that still bore his name. There being no particular hurry the journey took five full days. They were probably the last happy ones By was to spend. The Treasury was after his scalp.

It was sheer bad luck that the Duke was no longer Prime Minister, for the Duke would have looked after his own. Though he never saw Canada, he was thoroughly alive to the danger from the neighbour to the south, whether by open war or subversion. Two months after taking office, on 15 March, 1828, he had written to his old friend Lord Beresford, his successor as Master-General of the Ordnance, saying 'Let us make the Rideau Canal of a sufficient size to navigate steam vessels: that is the size proposed and estimated for by Lieut.-Col. By. This will give us the complete use of the Rideau .... Lieut.-Col. By might be desired to keep this object in view, and wherever he can do it without additional expense, he might lay his foundations, make his excavations, etc. accordingly.' Five days later he wrote to Mr Huskisson, Secretary for War and the Colonies, that £55,000 had been voted for the canal and something over £61,000 spent. The estimate for the whole business still stood at £420,000. 'It is very unfortunate that Lieut.-Col. By should not have waited for an answer before he proceeded so far in the execution of his works, as I am afraid that we must consequently go before Parliament with the whole case this year.' One may guess that the Duke would have had something to say to By behind closed doors but he would never have allowed one of his best and most deserving sapper officers to be hounded by politicians. Lord Grey and Lord John Russell, the civilians, took another view. By was ordered home to stand what amounted to a trial before a Parliamentary Committee. The best that can be said of the dreary business is that nobody actually accused him of lining his own pockets. One witness was John MacTaggart, who spoke up like a man in support of his old Chief. 'A gentleman I shall ever esteem and value. He encountered all privations with wonderful patience and good humour; was even too daring in some instances; would run rapids that his Indians trembled to look at; and cross wide lakes with the canoe when the Canadians were gaping with fear at the waves that were rolling around them.' The style is rather that of Mr Jingle but the sentiment comes through. MacTaggart had much more to say about the hardships he and By had endured and how their health had suffered from it. And he was eloquent about the matter of money. The Government had got a bargain.

The tone of it all hurt By deeply. He could reasonably have expected feats such as the ones he had just accomplished to be marked by, at least, a knighthood. He did not receive so much as a Vote of Thanks or an inscribed piece of plate. Very properly, he said not a word for public consumption.

His feelings were made plain, however, within the sapper family. A letter to his old friend Colonel Elias Durnford, RE, tells of them. 'The present Government throws blame on me for not waiting for the Parliamentary Grants, forgetting that it was ordered by His Grace, the Master-General, and Board that I was not to wait for Parliamentary Grants but to proceed with all dispatch consistent with economy; accordingly the contracts were formed by the Commissary-General at Montreal; by which the Engineering Department was bound to pay for the works as they proceeded, which precluded the possibility of stopping the works, and thus laying the Government open for heavy damages. I was never ordered to stop the works until I was so unjustly recalled when, thank God, they were all finished and the Canal had been open to the public for some months, or I should have been robbed of the honour of building the magnificent erection.'

The accusation that By had beaten the gun was less than just. In a debate on the Ordnance Estimates as long ago as 7 July, 1828,

Sir Henry Hardinge, the Duke's Commissioner to the Prussian Army at Waterloo and now his Secretary at War, had said flatly that 'Defence itself was an object of such importance that in 1826 he had received orders from the Duke of Wellington to bring forward the works in question. They had been assented to by Lord Liverpool.' Hardinge had served throughout the Peninsula, having first distinguished himself under Moore at Corunna, and was as much privy to the Duke's thoughts as any man. In due time he was himself to become Master-General of the Ordnance and, living as he did at South Park, Tunbridge Wells, he was a country neighbour to the Bys. With such information in his possession, as it must have been, By can hardly be accused of precipitate action in pressing ahead without formal resolutions from Parliament.

The home-keeping gentlemen who made up the Committee were harshly critical about estimates, a word to them suggesting the kind of thing provided by Cubitt for building a new house in Mayfair. By's last figure, given in 1831, had been for £800,000. The final bill came to £900,000; the difference was not vast and it was still uncommonly good value. Every tale of wrong calculations, of crookery by contractors and dishonesty everywhere was lapped up. The fault, no matter what had gone wrong, was always that of Colonel By. Both he and Colonel Durnford reckoned themselves discourteously treated and By himself was bitterly hurt. He wrote regularly to Durnford and told him all that was going on. In a letter from Shernfold written on 26 February, 1833, he explained that he had been to a levée. 'My old friend General Mulcaster was there. I told him I wished to be made a king's ADC for the sake of the rank, but he said that that required great interest.' Though this was something By lacked, he did at least touch the heights for one brief moment. 'The King appeared to remember me, asked how long I had been absent and if the canal was finished.' This was the only recognition By received for all his achievements. Other people were quite as angry as he, for Richard Bonnycastle wished to be excused his knighthood on the grounds that his friend was more deserving. Nothing, however, came of it. John and Esther By went back to Shernfold Park. There he died on 1 February, 1836, killed at 53 by the Canadian wilderness and the Westminster politicians.

The Rideau Canal was never used in war, but its presence must have been a comfort to Bonnycastle when he commanded at Kingston during the 1837 rebellion. Knowledge that he could be quickly reinforced, knowledge common to him and the rebels, enabled him to run his ship with a firm hand. The distinguished naval officer turned novelist Captain Marryat (whom we shall meet again) was visiting Canada at that time and, as in duty bound, offered his services to Sir John Colborne. 'It has been a sad scene of sacrilege, murder, burning and destroying,' he wrote home to his mother. 'All the fights have been in the churches and they are now burned to the ground and strewed with the wasted bodies of the insurgents.' Nothing like this happened in Kingston.

The military value of the canal continued to dwindle as the centre of gravity moved westwards. Only a mere four years were to elapse before the first railways appeared and the transformation of Canada into the world's granary began. Bytown, seemingly left behind, continued to grow steadily from a construction camp to a considerable trading centre with its emphasis on timber. By 1855 it has become important enough to be seriously considered as a capital city when the time should arrive for Canada to need one. When, in 1867, the moment of decision came there were, naturally enough, other claims put forward. In the end it was the Queen herself who was compelled to adjudicate; Ottawa (formerly Bytown) should be the capital of her new Dominion. The honour was, in some places, resented but time cures most things.

The Rideau Canal remains. Within the nation's capital it can be seen exactly as the builders left it, though decent retaining walls along each side have replaced the sloping earth banks for most of its length. The National Capital Commission plainly treasures it, with lovely gardens — notable for their tulips — on both sides and fine driveways. The memorials abound. Colonel By Island stands above the waters of Rideau Lake and near to the Entrance Locks is the Museum that bears his name. McTaggart (so spelt) has a street named after him, as do the sappers Bolton, Boteler and Pooley. The Historical Society of Ottawa commissioned the fine statue, unveiled in 1971 by the Governor-General with a guard of honour from the Royal Engineers. Though their canal saw no war service it has one claim that no other can make. During the winter months it makes the longest skating rink in the world. The long-dead sappers who worked on it would surely be pleased, especially the vindicated Colonel By. As Saul of old went out in search of his father's asses and found a kingdom, so did he set out to build a piece of military engineering work and founded one of the world's great cities.

1. 'The Shop'. 'Part of the building consisted of a tower, all that remained of a house once belonging to Prince Rupert'. (p. 10)

2. The Shop c. 1900.

3. Addiscombe when still the Military Seminary of the East India Company.

4. The Guard at Addiscombe c. 1840. (see p.11).

5. 'Famous within his Corps, but practically unknown outside it' – General Sir Charles Pasley. (p.16)

6. Colonel John By's statue in Ottawa. (p.37)

7. 'The Rideau, so named by early voyageurs from the curtain-like appearance of the falls at the Ottawa end'. (p.44) *(Burrowes No. 1)*

8. 'The bridge was to have eight spans in all… over the gap known as La Grande Chaudiere'. (p.46) *(Burrowes No. 8)*

9. The first eight locks of the Rideau Canal. *(Burrowes No. 13)*

10. Cranberry Lake – 'one of the most disagreeable places in the entire system'. (p.53) *(Burrowes No. 63)*

11. The Dam at Round Tail Falls 'where the Cataraqui River began its descent to Kingston'. (p.53) *(Burrowes No. 62)*

12. 'The outstanding pieces of work on the system were... and the Hog's Back Dam near Bytown'. (p.57) *(Burrowes No. 15)*

13. 'Jones Falls... the building of a 350-foot dam along with a flight of four locks is reckoned to be By's masterpiece'. (p.61) *(Burrowes No. 53)*

14. 'Arthur Thomas Cotton came of a family distinguished both in the Army and the Church'. (p.82)

15. All that remains of the Lower Anicut on the Coleroon River (see p.93)

16. Lieutenant Henry Spencer
Palmer, RE, 'showed early signs
of something uncomfortably like
genius'. (p.105)

17. Fort Colville on the Columbia River, 1862. (see p.117)

18. 'It had been agreed that the boundary should be the 49th parallel'. (p.107). One of the Sapper-built obelisks marking the parallel.

19. The Sinai survey party, 1868. (see p.128)

20. 'Colin Scott-Moncrieff
is one of the RE immortals'.
(p.148)

21. 'The Barrage was of the greatest importance but...'. (p.162)

22. 'Still only 21, Edmund Du Cane found himself in command of a
large force of convicts'. (p.169)

23. Fowke's masterpiece was the South Kensington Museum; the east dome 24 January, 1862. (p.179)

24. 'Cromwell Road (31 March, 1862) looks substantially unchanged, save only for the hansom cabs and absent motor traffic'. (p.179)

25. The Fowke Medal is still awarded for architectural pro-wess.

26. Major-General William Twiss. (see p.185)

27. The top of the Grand Shaft, showing the three staircases: 'Twiss's chef d'oeuvre'. (p.186)

28. Inside the light-well of the Grand Shaft, looking upwards.

29. The proposed Channel Tunnel, 1880.

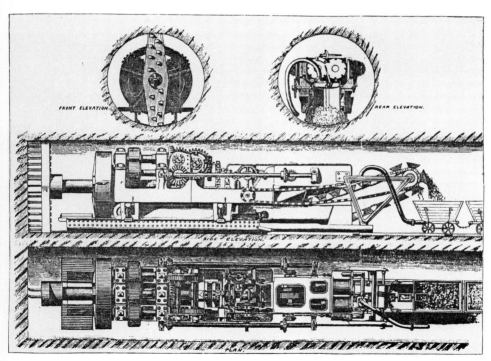

FRONT ELEVATION.

REAR ELEVATION.

SIDE ELEVATION.

PLAN.

30. Beaumont and English's compressed air tunnelling machine from
The Illustrated London News, 4 March, 1882.

31. Sir Gordon Guggisberg when
a Second Lieutenant; 'his name is
among the great ones of the
Corps'. (p.203)

32. Sir Gordon Guggisberg with the Duke and Duchess of Argyll.

IV

Epilogue in Australia

THOUGH BY'S CAREER ENDED with his Canal, those of some of his young men were only beginning. Edward Charles Frome, born in 1802, was the senior by a couple of years but William Denison rose higher in the service. Neither man has any enduring memorial in Canada but each has left his name permanently attached to some topographical feature somewhere. Frome has a lake and a road in South Australia: Denison an island in Sydney Harbour. Both, of course, have a form of immortality in the Professional Papers of the Royal Engineers. Denison was, indeed, more responsible than any other man for the series coming into existence, and was its first editor.

Their imprints upon the map of Australia came about in this way. Engineers had little to do with the early development of the even newer world since its formative years coincided with what men then called The Great War. The Duke had better use for his few sappers than planning public works at the other end of the earth. With Bonaparte safely settled in the sapper-maintained house in St. Helena more and more senior RE officers became available for empire-building. When the veteran Sir John Fox Burgoyne was asked by the young William Ewart Gladstone, in his last days as Colonial Secretary, to nominate a Governor for Van Diemen's Land he chose the recently knighted Sir William Denison. It was a routine posting after several years of work for the Admiralty. Frome had arrived several years earlier in order to clear up a remarkable mess. His specialité was trigonometrical surveying and soon after his return from Canada his book on the subject was published. It instantly became a standard work and went into several editions, the last being revised in 1873 by Sir Charles Warren. Colonel Frome was to need many skills additional to this one.

Edward Gibbon Wakefield had only a remote kinship with the

Captain of Hampshire Grenadiers and historian of the Roman Empire but his thoughts were of an imperial kind. They began unpromisingly. To seek to mend one's fortunes by carrying off the orphan daughter of a rich Canton merchant to Gretna Green may be, at 20, no more than natural exuberance. When the wife so acquired dies four years later and one makes the journey again with another heiress, overpersuaded by some economy of truth, the same plea will hardly avail. Mr Wakefield got three years; so did his brother William who had helped. Like Oscar Wilde, to whom he bore no other likeness, Mr Wakefield turned his enforced leisure towards literature. *Letter From Sydney* was a remarkable effort when one remembers that the author never had seen nor ever would see the subject of his animadversions. The reasoning behind his theme went something like this. Colonies — antipodean ones in particular — were making imperceptible progress. The reason was obvious. Only two classes of people, great landowners and convicts, were there to build a country. What Australia needed was a prosperous middle class with a sufficiency of servants and labourers to support it. Land should not be the subject of grants in great swathes; it ought to be sold off in small parcels to those who could afford to pay. On enlargement, Mr Wakefield sold his idea to Colonel Torrens, the political economist, who should on no account be confused with that other Colonel Torrens, Military Secretary successively to Sir Arthur Wellesley and the Duke of York. Torrens found the reasoning faultless and formed the South Australian Association for populating a new colony on the Wakefield system. If it seems barely credible that Torrens could be taken in by such stuff, and from such a man, remember that in another cell in Tothill prison resided Gregor MacGregor, once a General in the army of Simon Bolivar but now self-styled Prince of Poyais, a non-existent earthly paradise on the Coast of Honduras, to which some fifty settlers had been directed and to whose government the banking house of Perring & Co, with a former Lord Mayor as head, willingly lent £200,000. It was not merely the Golden Age of European colonization; it was also a time when anybody would believe anything about anything so long as it was far enough away. Mr Wakefield's part in the business was over. He had adventures enough ahead of him in Canada and New Zealand but he has no further part in this story.

A few miles inland from the Suffolk coast at Aldeburgh stands the village of Theberton. Even those who live there would not claim Theberton to be the most beautiful of its kind but it has had its moments of glory and its Norman church with the flinted round tower can stand up amongst the best. The great family of Theberton has for centuries been the Doughtys, whose chapel takes up much of the south side. Greatest amongst them is that Lieut.-Colonel Doughty-Wylie who won his posthumous Victoria Cross by mustering and leading a forlorn hope for the attack on Sedd-el-Bahr, the key to the Gallipoli peninsula. Thus was cemented an Australian connection, but Doughty-Wylie was not the first Theberton man to be remembered in the chronicles of that country.

It began with a traditional 18th century village scandal. Some time when George II was newly come to the throne, William Negus of Theberton, son to a substantial landowner, got his mother's maid, Mary Light, into trouble. Their son was packed off to the Navy as soon as he was big enough. After a spell lasting four years he left the service in India and set up, Conrad-style, as a trader in the waters around the Gulf of Siam. Being, as was obvious, gifted with powers of persuasion, Francis Light exercised them on the East India Company. In 1786 he negotiated a take-over bid for the island of Penang, the Sultan withdrawing from business in return for the Company's protection. Captain Light, as he was usually called, was made superintendent of the island. At almost exactly the same time Francis fathered a son. His mother, who may have been by then Mrs Light, was said (by Francis) to have been a Princess of the house of Kedah but unkind people have remarked that her name of Martinha Rozells suggests the Portuguese Eurasian. Be that as it may, their son William was born on 27 April, 1786, at Kuala Kedah and at the age of 6 was returned to Theberton as quickly as his father had been removed from it. Francis, who cannot have been ill-regarded for so trivial a slip, had kept up with his friends and neighbours, the Doughtys and Charles, the then head of the family, agreed to take care of the boy. William, like his father, served a short term in the Navy but did not persevere with the idea. By the Trafalgar year he was in Calcutta for his sister's wedding but he did not linger in India. As soon as Arthur Wellesley had landed in Mondego Bay William Light was with the Army Agents buying himself a pair of colours. The war in

Spain suited him. His talent for languages was invaluable, his upbringing in the East no disadvantage and he was often employed as go-between with the guerrilla bands of Mina, El Empecinado and the others. By the end of 1812 he had made himself enough of a name to be taken on the Duke's own staff as Intelligence Officer. Though lacking Shop education, he was a naturally skilful map-maker. William Light had a good war, being involved in forty battles of various sizes and emerging without a scratch.★ His father had died in 1794 but William's way of life in the post-war years suggest that he had been left a handsome patrimony. It would have been surprising otherwise, though it is said that his mother had been comprehensively swindled out of her great estates as soon as the Captain was no longer there. To make good any deficiency William respected tradition and married a bastard daughter of the 3rd Duke of Richmond. For the next three years things seem to have gone well enough and they cruised happily round the Mediterranean in their yacht, Light making some excellent sketches to pass the time. Two volumes, *Sicilian Scenery* and *Views of Pompeii,* were published in London. In 1830 they called at Alexandria where Light met Mehemet Ali, by then undisputed master of Egypt. His fleet having been sunk at Navarino three years earlier, the Pasha was looking for officers to furnish him with a new one. Light undertook to try and find some; as he sailed the yacht home for that purpose his wife left him for another man. Light, who does not seem to have been greatly distressed by this, returned in 1834 with a paddle-steamer, the *Nile,* which was to be the nucleus of a new Egyptian navy. That delivered at Alexandria, he met Captain Hindmarsh, RN, whose biographer says that he had come 'for the purpose of assuming a high position' in the Egyptian service. He never assumed it. Hindmarsh, as a young officer, had been England's Casabianca.

★ Napier in his *History of the War in the Peninsula* gives Light half a page to himself (Vol VI, p 614), something very rare for a junior officer. Before attacking towards Toulouse the Duke sent Light to ride through the French lines, to ascertain their strength and report back. This, with much ingenuity and courage, he managed to achieve and the battle was fought. Napier called Light 'distinguished by the variety of his attainment, an artist, musician, mechanist, seaman and soldier'. Light never knew of this public praise. He died some months before the book appeared.

As the original boy was standing on the burning deck of the French battleship *L'Orient,* Hindmarsh, his opposite number, was alone on the deck of HMS *Bellerophon* whence all but he had been swept away by *L'Orient's* last broadside. It was Hindmarsh who had cut *Bellerophon's* cable and sailed her out of danger just before *L'Orient* blew up. The next thirty odd years had been anti-climax. He and Light got on well enough at the first encounter. Sir Charles Napier, just resigned as Governor of the projected Colony of South Australia, was one of Light's friends. When Hindmarsh went home, which he did almost as soon as *Nile* had been handed over, he carried with him a letter from Light to Napier recommending Hindmarsh for Governor. Napier had already recommended Light to the Colonial Office. From this came little good. The Navy got in first.

In February 1836, Rear Admiral John Hindmarsh, RN, was duly appointed Governor of South Australia. One month previously William Light had been appointed his Surveyor-General. He made a swift journey from London and arrived off Kangaroo Island on 17 August. After several false starts the entrance to Port Adelaide River was found on 21 November and the first settlers appeared. The Admiral fared worse. His HMS *Buffalo* was a slower sailer than Light's *Rapid* and it was not until 28 December that the Admiral's party arrived. At Holdfast Bay, 'under a venerable gum-tree', he read out the first Order in Council creating South Australia a British Colony and then his own commission. It was a little late, but nobody was there to listen. Light had already decided on the site for a capital, 6 miles inland.

The new-style lady and gentleman colonists were not pleased. They had had a miserable voyage. *Buffalo* was an old navy transport, well advanced in decrepitude and personally commanded by the Admiral. They had been cramped, ill, hungry and thirsty; all this they had put up with because the future was so wonderful. When they disembarked, top-hatted and crinolined as some of them were, they found themselves stranded in a swamp with nobody willing or able to help. Nor was the new Governor captivated by the sight of his realm. The idea of a capital so far from the sea was unattractive. Light was exhausted by his travels in search of suitable places but kept his temper. The Admiral, having no other adviser, agreed that this was where the city must go up, but he had reservations. On the third day after landing, the name of Adelaide, after the recently widowed Queen sometimes called 'the nicest Princess to have come out of Germany', found its way on to the map.

The sister colony of Victoria had found more trouble in naming its capital and there had been far less unanimity. During the building time it had been just 'the city' but as time went by and a decision had to be reached, more than one proposal was made. The custom of taking names from distant Royalty, or even remote grandees like the Duke and his senior commanders, was well established. On the other hand a strong case could be made for perpetuating the names of the pioneers. On the banks of the Yarra at the very beginning the Romulus and Remus had been Mr Fawkner and Mr Batman. The last-named having died young, a newspaper suggested keeping his memory green with the name 'Batmania'. It might have done well enough for a cricket ground but the Batmania Cup would never have sounded quite right. Instead the not outstandingly famous Lord Melbourne became immortal.

At Adelaide, as soon as the name had been settled, everybody broke out quarrelling. Mr Wakefield's ideas of an antipodean Home County demonstrably did not work, the colony was nearly bankrupt and would have to suffer thorough reorganization. How this all came about is a tale told elsewhere. So far as it concerns us, Light went ahead with surveying the unbuilt capital, laying out something over 1,000 acres in three months, while the Admiral meditated a change. As time went by he came to dislike Light's city more and more; all efforts to appease him by laying out something smaller at Port Adelaide availed nothing. Hindmarsh fulminated as only an Admiral can, while Light carried on as best he could with surveying and mapping the hinterland. The result showed the unwisdom of giving professional's work to amateurs, no matter how gifted. The men sent out with Light were not up to the job, they were hopelessly under-equipped and badly underpaid. Light sent Kingston, his deputy, home to seek help from the Colonial Office, the most important piece of it being the removal of Admiral Hindmarsh. It was a waste of time. The Secretary of State was Lord Glenelg, of whom one may fairly say that, against some strong competition, he was the worst Colonial Secretary of all time. His contribution to the affairs of South Australia was less disastrous than those he bestowed on South Africa and Canada; probably because an empty continent gave inadequate scope to his talents for disorganization. The Admiral was indeed recalled and went to see what he could achieve as Lieutenant-Governor of Heligoland. Kingston was ordered to give up his proper trigonometrical surveying and content himself with something cruder and cheaper. Light, utterly disenchanted, resigned. It was brave of him, for the gesture left him rat-poor, living in a half-built house, miserably ill and cared for by his old friend Maria Gandy. His only income was from an occasional sale of one of his sketches. In October, 1839, he died and was buried in the city square named after him. It was a miserable end, at only 52, for a man who had been a cavalry, infantry and intelligence officer, a fine linguist, a competent seaman, talented musician and accomplished artist. Nor did he forget his origins. He called his house Thebarton, which was probably phonetically right. East Anglia does drawl out its vowel sounds. Saint Peter's church at Theberton remembers him equally well. Shown alongside the bits and pieces of a Zeppelin shot down nearby in 1917 are all that remains in the way of his memorabilia. Adelaide, regarding him as the city's true founder, has fixed his place in history with a Light Square, a statue and his own self-portrait in the National Gallery. All these things are deserved, for William Light was a man to be admired. There is also, perhaps, a moral in the tale. Had Light been a regular, Shop-trained Engineer officer with access to those at the head of the Corps, particularly Sir Charles Pasley, his emissary might have carried more weight with the Colonial Office and much grief averted. It always pays to employ a professional.

The Admiral's successor, Colonel Gawler, arrived in October, 1838, accompanied by the new Surveyor-General, Captain Sturt. Each had a distinguished career behind him in the Peninsula; George Gawler had, in addition, commanded the flank company of Colborne's 52nd which, at Waterloo, had given the coup de grace to the Old Guard. Both were infantrymen, untrained to engineering and innocent of political skills.

Early in the following year the professionals arrived, a party of regular Sappers commanded by Captain Frome. Colonel Gawler was brutally removed in 1841, being told of his dismissal by the man who had come to replace him. George Grey was better fitted for the appointment, being only 29 and temperamentally suited to govern a new settlement. The previous four years he had spent in Western Australia and he had a better grasp than his predecessors of what his new viceroyalty needed. For a start he gave Captain Frome carte blanche to carry out the survey as seemed best to him. It was soon being made in proper Woolwich fashion and the cost of it came down with a run.

Edward Frome was employed in the Colony for the following ten years in the dual capacities of Surveyor-General and Colonial Engineer. Under his guidance all the amenities of civilization burgeoned, with roads, bridges and a rather fine prison. In 1849 he handed the baton to another sapper, Arthur Henry Freeling, and returned home to retirement as Knight and Major-General. As mentioned before, a road and a lake in South Australia each bear his name.

Freeling, in the dozen years between 1849 and 1861, oversaw the growth of Adelaide from infancy to lusty youth. As Chairman of the Board set up to run the city, he had a finger in every pie. Harbour works and water supply, road building and river navigation, trams from Port Adelaide to the sea beach, mineral development and copper mining, even the purchase of the guns for Fort Glanville, all of them were Freeling's business. And when he went home to become Major-General Sir Arthur the Colony had still not seen the last of the Royal Engineers. Ten years later Colonel William Francis Drummond Jervois, RE, was posted to Australia in order to examine such defences as there might be. He was raised to the rank of Governor of South Australia in 1877, having served his apprenticeship under Harry Smith in South Africa, as inspector of the fortifications of Canada during the American Civil War and as Governor of Singapore during the early '70s. When his time in South Australia was up, Jervois, now Lieut-General Sir William, was translated to New Zealand. For a Corps never numerically very large the Royal Engineers furnished a great many Colonial Governors and high officials. The quality of Shop training went far beyond the merely military.

If you cast your mind back to the Rideau Canal you will remember Lieutenant Denison, lately Governor of Van Diemen's Land. Before becoming Lieutenant-General Sir William, he had further services to perform far away from Canada. His Australian period covered some fifteen years, beginning with his appointment as Lieutenant-Governor of Tasmania in 1847, an appointment he owed to John Fox Burgoyne. His seven years there, being mainly concerned with internal politics, have no place here. In 1854 he was promoted Governor of New South Wales, a rank that also carried with it the proud but meaningless title of Governor-General of Australia. Once again Denison's activities, however animating, were political rather than constructional and in 1861 he moved yet further up the ladder as Governor of Madras. In the immediate aftermath of a great military mutiny a tight hand was needed and Denison's reputation as a disciplinarian stood high.

In India he ran true to form, being still persuaded that benevolent despotism was the only way to run such a country. He had suffered much from low-grade politicians in Australia; once was enough for any man. When the idea was propounded that the higher reaches of the Civil Service be filled by competitive examination he was properly scornful. 'If there is one quality which is more required in India then elsewhere it is that which makes a man a gentleman,' he wrote in reply. The supply of gentlemen was running slowly out and not all the players won Sir William's approval. Practically everything he did or said, according to the composer of his *Dictionary of National Biography* entry, was governed by the words 'disapproved' or 'deprecated'. It does not necessarily follow that he was always wrong. For a time, following the sudden death of Lord Elgin, Colonel Sir William Denison became Acting Governor-General; this effectively ended his service career. On returning home he was told that an ex-Viceroy, even an acting one who had been in post only for a couple of months, was far too grand to hold a mere Colonel's appointment. Denison retired, was raised to the rank of Lieutenant-General and devoted the rest of his life — he died in 1871 — to Chairmanship of a Royal Commission on the prevention of river pollution. No doubt it made a change.

V

General Cotton and the Irrigation of India

IT IS NOT COMMONPLACE for a nation recently relieved of government by foreigners to erect a statue in honour of one of them. Soon after India regained independence in 1947 those of kings and queens and generals put up over the years by successive British administrations came tumbling down; that is hardly remarkable. What is remarkable is the fact that nearly forty years later the Government of Andhra Pradesh, one of the major States of India, of its own accord erected a statue to one of the foreigners and unveiled it with much ceremony. In the words of a retired Chief Engineer of Eastern Command, the subject was 'not a great soldier, or a statesman, but a great engineer'. It came about in this fashion.

Recent history, say that of the last three centuries, apart, everything in India can trace itself back so far in time that one becomes dazzled by sheer antiquity. We in England tend to think of recorded history beginning with Homer and the Trojan War. Something like 1500 years before Homer was born, about the same time span as separates us from King Arthur, the Indus Valley was one of the great civilizations of the ancient world. Its people, whoever they may have been, lived in fine cities, well planned, skilfully built and, one must suppose, ruled by a regular government. Not merely all evidence but even all memory and tradition concerning it vanished at some distant but indeterminate time until Mohenjo Daro and Harappa were excavated only a few decades back. No man now living can say with certainty how all this came to vanish from the face of the earth and, inevitably, there is more than one opinion. The most persuasive, held by General Rau and others in a position to speak with authority, is that the

78

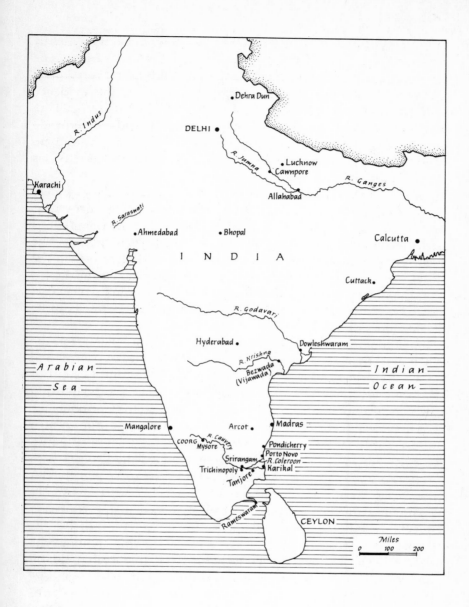

reason was military. The invaders, probably the earliest of the Aryan tribes, were tougher, better armed and more warlike. The horse, then unknown in India, had been made to serve them, a fact borne out by the few remaining pieces of tangible evidence found among the ruins. Presumably, like all barbarians everywhere and always, the destruction of fine cities satisfied them and they left the remains to the vulture and the desert. They would no more have taken them over as going concerns than did the Britons when Rome marched out.

Another informed opinion, that of the retired Chief Engineer (Irrigation), is that the river beds rose and the cities were drowned. It is certain, as Sir Mortimer Wheeler found, that the foundations of Mohenjo Daro are well below the present water level. The theories are not irreconcilable. First the fire and sword, then the flood. Combined, they made certain that nothing remained.

In the nature of things, the cities of the valley could never have existed without elaborate works of irrigation; not a trace can be found. India guards her mysteries well.

Irrigation has always been a more important matter for the inhabitants than any other aspect of life. There are, of course, and always have been rivers, from the mighty Indus and Ganges to the humblest village brook. And almost as much as the existing rivers there remain ghosts of rivers long forgotten. Consider, for example, the Saraswati. For thousands of years, time almost unimaginable to a westerner, Hindu mythology has insisted on the existence of a third river which also joined the Ganges with the Jumna by Allahabad. As there was no river to be perceived it was called 'gupt' — the unseen — but belief in its existence remained unshaken in the face of all evidence to the contrary. Everybody but the pious Hindu assumed the story to be just another of those legends that proliferate throughout the sub-continent. Until early in the year 1988. In a search for oil near Dehra Dun the engineers struck water where no water should have been. They are now tolerably confident that they have stumbled across a part of the long-lost Saraswati and that it does indeed run underground for some 2,000 miles from the Himalayas roughly parallel with the Ganges and emptying itself also into the Bay of Bengal. The discovery coincided with the severest drought for a century and it is hoped that the worst of northern India's irrigation difficulties will be ended. One theory, as yet unproved, is that the Saraswati once watered the ancient communities and that its disappearance caused what is now the desert of Thar. It is easy to suggest what took place after the river had vanished: no convincing explanation has been put forward as to why it did so. Such things happen in India and the old legends may not safely be disregarded. There are other instances apart from the Saraswati.

The British connection with India began with the formation of the East India Company in 1600, long after the irruption of both Portuguese and Dutch. It was simply a trading venture on a large scale and was no business of governments. The Portuguese were not unduly distressed at handing over Bombay to Charles II as part of the dowry of his wife, Catherine of Braganza. The King, with no greater sense of loss, promptly turned it over to the Company. In the south the Company's agent, Mr. Day, rented from the Rajah of Carnatic for £600 a year a parcel of land which found little favour with his employers. 'It was nothing but a dreary waste of sand, on which a monstrous sea broke in a double line of surf, giving it an inhospitable look which it retains to the present day.' It acquired the name of Madras. In 1690 the Viceroy of Bengal, subordinate to the Moghul Emperor in Delhi, leased to the Company's man Job Charnock three villages named Sutanati, Govindapur and Kalikata. Only the last name remains.

For a long time the greatest European activity occurred in the South, with the Anglo-French conflicts associated with the names of Clive and Dupleix as in Canada they were with Wolfe and Montcalm. Then in 1757 came Plassey and a choice was forced upon the Company. Either it must allow India to be taken over by an assortment of robber barons who would put an end to all trade or it must somehow administer the country itself. This it began to do. The task was beyond the resources of private men and the government in London agreed to sit in. The Company had an army of its own, British-officered and Indian-manned, but it was not enough. King's regiments and batteries arrived and the two served side by side in the campaigns against Tipu Sahib at Seringapatam and the Mahratta chieftains who had other ideas on India's future. The Indian campaigns were a proving ground for senior British general officers: the Duke himself, after Assaye, did not disdain the label of 'a sepoy general'. Nor was he unmindful of considerations more tangible than mere reputation. In old age he confided to Miss Burdett Coutts that 'I do wear muslin next to my skin . . . I wear the finest Bengal muslin if I can find any'.★

To furnish a regular intake of young military officers the Company, in 1809, set up its own Academy at Addiscombe, near Croydon. In an existence of litttle over fifty years, for it died with the Company after the Mutiny, it produced some notable men. In England the most famous names are Roberts and Napier of Magdala. India better remembers Arthur Cotton, for it was his statue that was put up as a sign of what General Rau calls 'reverence and respect'. As said before, occurrences like this are not common.

Arthur Thomas Cotton came of a family distinguished both in the army and the Church. The most illustrious member, and head of the house, was Sir Stapleton, the only cavalry commander in the Peninsula whom the Duke had come even halfway towards trusting to do what he was told. Sir Stapleton, raised to the peerage in 1814 as Baron Combermere, had an uncle, Henry Calveley Cotton of Woodcote in Oxfordshire. The philoprogenitive Mr Cotton sired twelve children and his energy was not mis-directed. Among the number of his sons five became important figures in national affairs. The eldest, Sydney, was born in 1792, served in India and Australia for many years mostly as a cavalry officer, rose to the rank of Lieutenant-General and ended his days in 1874 as Governor of Chelsea Hospital. Others included Admiral Francis Vere Cotton, General Frederick Cotton, another Sapper and of whom more presently, and Richard Lynch Cotton, sometime Provost of Worcester College, Oxford. A cousin, George Edward Lynch Cotton, was the son of another of Sir Stapleton's uncles, Captain Thomas Cotton of the 7th Fusiliers, killed at the Battle of the Nivelle a fortnight after his son's birth. After serving for a spell as an usher at Rugby under Dr Arnold (he was 'the young master' of *Tom Brown's Schooldays)* he became Master of Marlborough from which appointment he was translated into becoming Bishop of Calcutta in 1858. After eight years during which he did his best to mitigate the absurdities of Macaulay's ideas on the education of Indians he had the misfortune to fall from a steamer's gangway into the Ganges and was never seen

★ *Angela Burdett-Coutts* by Clara Burdett Patterson, John Murray, 1953, p. 81.

again. General Sir Willoughby Cotton, yet another cousin, had been ringleader of the famous Rugby mutiny in 1797 when the boys attempted to burn down the school after blowing in the headmaster's door with gunpowder. That accomplished, he joined the 3rd Guards, served all through Spain under the Duke and, in 1821, became colonel of the 47th in India. His last exploit, almost as famous as his first, was to command a column during the invasion of Afghanistan in 1839. He was fortunate in being withdrawn before disaster struck. Sir Willoughby had but two children, though one, Corbet, inevitably became a General in his turn. India saw a lot of the Cottons.

Arthur Thomas, the subject of this memorial, was born on 15 May, 1803, at the Cotton family seat, Combermere Abbey, near Whitchurch in Shropshire. As his father had many mouths to feed one cannot affect surprise at Arthur being packed off to the East India Company's Military Academy at the age of 15. This was not regarded as unusual. Addiscombe took boys in at that early stage of life, subjected them to a two-year course much on Shop lines and commissioned them usually before their 17th birthdays. Only the first few cadets in the passing-out list became Engineers. Arthur was one of them and, in 1819, at the age of 16½ was duly gazetted to the Madras Engineers. In accordance with custom he was given some practical experience before being shipped off, first with the Ordnance Survey at Bangor and then at the Sapper heartland of Chatham. It is possible that Sir Stapleton had something to do with Arthur being sent to the Madras Presidency for he had been there before. It was at the siege of Tipu's fortress at Seringapatam in 1799 that the 26-year-old Lieutenant-Colonel Cotton had first met Colonel Arthur Wellesley and obviously made a good impression on him. From this had come all his subsequent preferment. Nor had India seen the last of him. In May, 1825, Baron Combermere, Commander-in-Chief, India, achieved what Sir Gerard Lake had failed to do twenty years earlier. The Jat fortress of Bhurtpore had long posed a standing threat to British rule. 'Little Cotton', as they had called him in Spain, decided that this must be eliminated for good. Lake had taken the place at the sixth attempt but the owners had been allowed to rent it back. This time it would be different. Cotton's Sappers prepared and fired a huge mine and the fortress was then stormed. Baron Combermere became Viscount Combermere on the strength of it. He returned home in 1830 and remained busy for many years, his last public appearance being as Gold Stick in Waiting at the wedding of the Prince of Wales and Princess Alexandra.

His young cousin Arthur embarked for India in May, 1821: five months later he landed through the surf at Madras. Arthur should not have felt lonely. His elder brother Sydney, with several years of cavalry service behind him, was there as DAA & QMG. Shortly afterwards Sydney exchanged into The Buffs and went to join them in New South Wales. There he stayed for six years, returning to Calcutta with his regiment in the first weeks of 1828 and becoming Military Secretary to his cousin Lord Combermere.

Arthur, at the age of an Oxford freshman, took up his duties as an assistant engineer. These can scarcely have been arduous, for Madras had become a military backwater and now produced no more history than it could consume locally. The climate was agreeable, if one could stand the heat, the scenery splendid and the inhabitants peaceable. The first task assigned to him was interesting without stretching his professional abilities beyond bearing. The island of Rameswaram, off the south-east coast of India, is separated from it by a narrow channel (long since spanned by a railway bridge) known as the Pamban Passage. The young Cotton was charged with the duty of examining it with a view to having dredging work done that would enable ships of a size larger than was then usual to navigate through it in safety. Pottering about in a boat, taking soundings and making copious notes all under a warm sun can hardly have been unendurable hardship. Cotton duly reported that the thing could be done easily enough and on his recommendation the passage was deepened from 4½ feet to 10. The result of this shortening of the voyage from Tanjore to Colombo was to cut the cost of transit of goods to a third of what it had been. Within a few years traffic had increased twelve-fold. The dredging was not Cotton's work, for he was soon posted as assistant to Captain Fullerton, Superintending Engineer of the Southern Department, to acquaint himself with the business of tanks.

This was Cotton's introduction to irrigation, for tanks — great reservoirs held in by banks of earth — meant life to most Indian villages. If the monsoon failed, as it sometimes did, the sight of

84

cracked mud at the tank bottom could mean death. From the earliest times men had sought to press the rivers into service by diverting a network of artificial streams on to the fields but, as in other lands of ancient civilization, they had been allowed to fall into disrepair and the lack of water was already the heaviest burden the Dravidian population — descendants of the earliest known inhabitants of India — had to bear. Before Cotton could take a hand in bettering their situation he was called away.

The Burmese, like the Tamils of southern India, are good-natured people with a considerable sense of fun. Their philosophy, however, was not that of the Directors of the Company and artificial boundaries meant nothing to them. By 1824 they had penetrated more ore less peacefully to within 150 miles of Calcutta, causing something like panic among the Indian merchants. On one famous occasion the entire mercantile population had taken to its heels and sought refuge under the guns of Fort William. The Company, trying to be paternal, sent several warnings that the joke had gone too far and demanded that the Burmese put a stop to their incursions. Quite naturally they took no notice. Starting wars was no longer something within the Company's power, but the directors having persuaded themselves that the Burmese deserved punishment laid the matter before the Cabinet. What happened there is part of our folklore. The Cabinet, inevitably, sought advice from the ex-Sepoy General. The Duke gave it without hesitation. On being asked who should command the expedition he replied instantly 'Lord Combermere', then Commander-in-Chief in Ireland. 'But we have always understood that your grace thought Lord Combermere a fool.' 'So he is, and a damned fool; but he can take Rangoon.' Very possibly the Duke was playing the buffo part then expected of him. In 1812, after Cotton had sustained a serious wound to his arm, the Duke had written to Torrens, the Military Secretary, that 'Sir Stapleton Cotton has gone home. He commands our cavalry very well — indeed much better than some that might be sent to us and might be supposed cleverer than he is.' He had wanted Cotton to lead his horsemen at Waterloo and was not pleased at being given Lord Uxbridge instead. On the day after the battle, Uxbridge having lost his leg,* the Duke wrote again.' 'We must have Lord

* Lord Uxbridge's leg has its own tomb close by the battlefield. For many years it had

Combermere if he will come.' He came indeed, but by then the war was over. The Duke had fought his last battle, but Stapleton Cotton still had more ahead of him. Though he succeeded another Paget, Sir Edward, as Commander-in-Chief, India, in 1825 he was too late for the first Burma campaign. It was entrusted to Sir Archibald Campbell with 11,000 men and a naval force that, on the retirement hurt of Commodore Grant, was led by somebody we have met before. Captain Frederick Marryat gave up command of HM sloop *Larne* to become Senior Naval Officer, Rangoon.

The First Burma War was unlike any other war experienced by the Indian Army, King's and Company's regiments alike. In every past conflict the enemy had stood up, or run away, and provided something recognisable as a battle. The Burmese had better sense. They abandoned Rangoon, leaving nothing behind that was worth having, and dug themselves in. Laying siege to well-constructed stockades was sapper business and, as usual, sappers were thin on the ground. Lieutenant Cotton was summoned from his tanks to design and construct parallels and saps. One's sympathies must lie with the Burmese. David Hannay, Marryat's biographer, tells of how the Navy had to work at clearing the Irrawaddy of war-boats, transporting troops, protecting their landings and 'now and then helping storm a stockade, or beat down the fire, of native batteries mounted with guns that would not fire, handled by gunners who could not shoot. The enemy fought fiercely, according to his lights, but then he had neither good weapons, nor discipline, nor experience. Except when attacked in a particularly strong position, by an insufficient force, the poor Burmese were sent into action as cattle to slaughter.' The poor Burmese, of course, were not the real enemy. 'The operations dragged on for months, till fevers, cholera and scurvy had almost annihilated our army and had almost unmanned our squadron.' Fevers and scurvy were nothing new. Cholera, in regular armies, was. The 11,000 men landed in May — a few days after Cotton's 21st birthday — and by October they were down to 1,300 fit for duty. The Burmese were equally badly affected. As Campbell marched the 125 miles towards Prome his

as resident custodian, a Sergeant-Major Cotton. I have been unable to trace any relationship. His house is now the Cinema Naporama.

column went day after day through the jungle that then covered the land seeing no enemy but dying men. Often they had to clear away the corpses before camp could be made. Another force of 11,000 landed in the Arakan and had to be withdrawn without firing a shot by reason of sickness. In the British battalions engaged, six out of every seven men died. The British Army has no pleasant memories of Arakan. It was not the last visit.

In these dismal conditions Arthur Cotton acquitted himself well. He was in Rangoon when the counterattack came and watched amazedly as 30,000 Burmese dug themselves into the ground and disappeared from sight within a couple of hours. That done, they seemed to feel that honour had been satisfied and went home again. For much of the time he worked with Marryat's gunboats and, as the only Sapper officer in his column, led the stormers in attacks on no less than seven defended stockades. At one of these, Donbew, he came under the orders of Cousin Willoughby, by then a Brigadier. Arthur Cotton's last battle took place at Tavoy, where the Tenasserim peninsula verges upon Siam, and when the war ended in February, 1826, he returned to Madras. His services earned him a mention in despatches but his health, never outstandingly robust, had been undermined and was for many years to come something less than reliable.

A picture survives of the young subaltern at about this time. Like most Cottons, he was slightly built with a cavalryman's figure, his hair was dressed in the Byronic fashion of the day and the uniform of his Corps, all frogs and brandenburgs, was flamboyant. Nothing could have been more misleading. Arthur Cotton, except in the matter of superficial appearance, had nothing in common with the poet. His way of life was almost puritan, his devotion to his service and to India complete and his mind severely professional, mitigated by flashes of genius. The word, never one to be lightly employed, is used several times by his contemporaries and professional peers. Whether Cotton would have accepted the compliment is doubtful. He would probably have preferred to say that he never found difficulty in perceiving the obvious.

The next two years were comparatively uneventful. Lord Combermere went home to honourable retirement. His young kinsman, after some sick leave, was set to the work which became his life and upon which his fame rests. Once the Burma campaign was over he never again saw action, except against those other enemies mentioned in the book of Revelation, famine, sickness and sudden death.

The Madras Presidency, like some other parts of India, needed all the servants she could find, for life among the peasantry who made up most of the population was hard indeed. The ryot has always been a figure of affection for the British, even though too many of their memsahibs were inclined to treat him at best as a favourite dog or at worst as something not quite human. The Madrassi subsistence farmer was expert at his job; after so many generations working the same patch of land he ought to have been. Nevertheless, he had two deadly enemies. Relations between English farmers and their bank managers are commonly less than cordial but even the most exigent banker had much to learn from the Indian money-lender. The second, even less predictable, was the monsoon. Between the pair of them the cultivator's life was, in the most literal sense, precarious. Prayers to the bunnia might, just occasionally, lead to some slight let-up: those to whatever gods he believed to control the elements, never. Once a crop was carried in there was no knowing whether there would be a next one. It was all a matter of water. The rivers of what was loosely called the Carnatic were plenty and in good years bountiful. Even in the best of them, however, most of it ran to waste. In the north there still remained traces of irrigation systems made by the Moghul Emperors and, in the south, those made by the Chola kings in the 1st century A.D., as well as those made by the Kakatiya Kings in the 9th and 10th centuries and Vijayanagar Kings in the 14th and 15th centuries. As a consequence of bad relations between the kingdoms, however, and poor land communications for the distribution of food grains, these works were barely sufficient to meet the needs of the growing population. From the beginning of time it had been taken for granted that if the rains failed men, women and especially children would starve. Presumably this was the will of whatever gods there might be and it was nobody's business to do anything about it. The Company, which had a white side as well as a black, decided otherwise. The English — one has to use the word as a foreigner would use it — who were already in service there, whether civil or military, were, for the most part, but with some notable exceptions, of good quality, from Governor-General down to the last-arrived private soldier. Taken in the round, they liked and respected the Indians with whom they had to mix and the *de haut en bas* attitute was not common. Few, if any, of Macaulay's 'rich, quiet and infamous' remained. Later, for some inexplicable reason, a lower class of person, many of them frankly jumped-up, began to arrive and attitudes changed. People in a position to know put this down as one of the causes of the Mutiny in 1857. By 1830 the Company was consolidating and developing its assets. Far away in Assam, a mere geographical name for unsurveyed jungle, the servants of the first tea company were cutting and clearing in preparation for the great industry that still hardly existed. In Cotton's parish the business was water. To this day — or at any rate until quite recently — the only thing given away free in India is a refreshing draught from the iron tanks wheeled around railway stations by company employees. Nothing else approaches it in importance. Food comes a long way behind.

First of the rivers to be tamed was the Cauvery. It rises in the hills of Coorg, passes through the princely state of Mysore, and when a few miles above Trichinopoly splits into two streams. The larger, under the name of Coleroon, inclines more or less half-left until it flows into the Bay of Bengal by Porto Novo. The lesser, still called the Cauvery, swings half-right and joins the sea south of the French settlement of Karikal. In the triangle are many streamlets and, in 1828, irrigation in the lower reaches was reasonably adequate. Then, for no obvious reason, the waters of the Cauvery began to desert the southern part and to flow almost entirely along the Coleroon. Even worse was the fact that the 'noble river' — the words are Cotton's — Cauvery appeared to be drying up. In 1827 he was sent to carry out a detailed examination and the results were not encouraging. 'I was sent to inspect the work as the people were said to be nearly in a state of rebellion from its neglect. I found the works in utter disrepair: the Coleroon canal had 6 feet of silt in its bed, so that when it ought to have had 8 feet of water flowing down it had 2. 100,000 people depended on it.' The 'works' were trumpery affairs. From time out of mind the various governments had made feeble efforts to dam the river but only with the object of spreading the monsoon rain as widely as possible.

No attempt had been made to conserve water for use once the monsoon was over. This meant that from January to October the ryot had to depend on whatever had been collected in the tanks, which was precious little. In 1804 a Colonel Caldwell had been given the task of improving upon this but he had not accomplished anything of much use. Cotton's quick mind saw at once what needed to be done. 'The work of chiefest importance was the Upper Anicut (dam in English), constructed across the head of the Coleroon.' Cotton did some sums, estimated that it could be done for quite a modest outlay and sought out the Chief Engineer who took him to the Governor. The Governor seemed well disposed and authorized Cotton's £3,500 to be spent. That done, Captain Cotton returned to his other duties. As yet he had not acquired the perfect understanding of the ways of Company government that he was later to acquire. His belief that the work would now be put in hand was misplaced. The Governor gave instructions to the Collector. The Collector, or his clerks, wrote it all down. Thereafter he did nothing about it. Cotton learnt this for the first time when he came back to the job in 1833. 'Such was the inconceivable state of things in that admirable middle-class government.'

Those who look askance at the English class system — an odd word for anything so unsystematic — miss the only point that matters. It works. Had the assistant engineer of 1830 been Lieutenant Buggins whose parents had almost starved themselves in order to send him to Addiscombe, the irrigation of southern India would have had to wait far longer than it did. Lieutenant Cotton, cousin to Generals one of whom was Commander-in-Chief, Peer of the Realm and personal friend to the Duke, was different. Buggins might have been invited to a second-class dinner with the Collector; just possibly, in lean times, he might even have been bidden to the Governor's table along with Junior Merchants and such-like. His speech, if any, would have been limited to expressions of gratitude at such condescension. Not so Lieutenant Cotton. Only considerations of good manners would have prevented him from saying what he thought and a wise official would not have answered with anything that might have been held against him by the grandees in Calcutta or London. This did not prevent the young engineer from forming a very adverse opinion of the

Company's management of affairs so far as they touched the native population. It soon became plain to him that all that could be expected of the officials, from top to bottom, was a fairly efficient collection of revenue in the shape of land tax and water dues. In most places the Treasuries were bulging with rupees but any suggestion that some of them might be spent on public works that would improve land values — it would have been futile to add anything about improving living conditions — was met with a firm 'Can't afford it'.

Many years later, Cotton wrote a book. Probably the only surviving copy is in the India Office Library. It bears no title, no name of publisher or printer and can only be dated by his mentioning 'this year of 1852'. Inside the fly-leaf is a signature that looks like 'H. D. Seymour' and the contents are annotated in places by pencilled entries in the margin. The thrust of it is that India needed, and had long needed, both irrigation and cheap communications, preferably by canal rather than railway. '2 out of 4 people are employed in growing food and a 3rd in carrying goods. By irrigation 1 could grow food for 4 and by the cheap transit 1 could carry food for 40.' The official attitude to any serious public works was marked by 'Man's determination not to go into the water until he can swim.' Cotton had a gift for similes and metaphors. They are many more like this. Equally there are plain statements of fact.

'To an Engineer in India intent on public improvements, this is the thing that continually weighs him down, that he is compelled to feel at every step he takes that he is not transacting business with a fellow Englishman but with a white native, whose views of things are those imbibed within the air that he has breathed in his cutcherry for 10, 20 or 30 years.' They had no interest in welfare, only in land tax. 'For my part, so heartily sick and ashamed I am when I look at the present wretched state of these millions so long under the Government of a Christian, civilized nation that I should like to have an Act passed that no man should be in Court, Council or Board, no one to be Governor or Head of a Department, who had been more than 15 years in India and that half should never have been in India at all.' He mentions 'a Collector with some lakhs of rupees deficient in the cash chest.' Pencilled in the margin, presumably by Mr Seymour, is 'Rouse Peter of Madura who when found out drank laudanum.' It was not only Company men who came under the whip. When writing of the River Godavari before he took it in hand Cotton observed that it was 'not navigated at all by boats, no doubt owing to the uncontrolled powers of the petty zemindars on its banks who assume the right of demanding dues on everything that passes.' He mentions the Rideau Canal, open for only a few months in the year but paying its way for lack of zemindars. In all probability his informant was Sir John Franklin with whom he had stayed in Tasmania during 1839 when Franklin was Governor. There is much in the book about waterways, including 'Mr Ellet's remarkable report on the Mississippi.' On India he had nothing good to say. The Government was 'keeping the country in a beggarly state. It will be starved to death while the railroads are constructing.' Against that, not less than 5,000 miles of river navigation could be made at no great cost.

The only source of information about Arthur Cotton's activities during the early 1830s comes from a biography written by his daughter, Lady Hope, and published in 1890. Like most Victorian ladies the authoress was strong on moral philosophy but sparing with dates. Cotton certainly came home on sick leave at the beginning of 1830, leaving his young brother Fred as deputy. Lady Hope has much to say about his eschewal of such traditional sports as hunting, shooting and wenching and gives interesting information about his attitude to matters spiritual. He seems to have suffered from recurrent fever, something known more recently to those who have served in Burma, but unlike them he underwent no treatment of any value. Sir John Fortescue implies that quinine was unknown in India at the time. In any event, the return journey took over a year. Cotton decided to carry it out in the most difficult way possible. After crossing France he took an Italian brig to Beirut and made his way back to India overland, suffering a bout of fever in Persia that nearly killed him. The current regulations denied him any further home leave and for the next few years he took it in Tasmania where he met the lady who was to become his wife. It seems impossible to give dates with anything approaching accuracy, but that cannot greatly matter now.

On returning to Madras in 1833, where he was greeted by the faithful Fred, Cotton was once more set to work on the Cauvery. There had been bad years in southern India during his absence. 1831 had brought a huge monsoon followed by floods: 1832 produced cyclones which devastated the crops: the monsoon of 1833 was worse than disappointing, for hardly any rain fell at all. A little further north, along the Godavari, it was called the year of the Great Famine. Something drastic had to be done, Collector or no Collector. Fortunately for many people, the hour, as it so often does, produced the man. The Royal Engineers Journal for 1 September, 1890, tells of it.

'No one conceived the remedy until Captain Cotton, with the insight of genius, combined with high professional qualifications, addressed himself to the task of utilizing the system of rivers to the greatest practicable extent. No works on anything like the scale of those now projected by Captain Cotton had been undertaken in India before his time, so that every detail of their construction had to be determined de novo by himself.' These last few words sum up Sir Arthur Cotton's main claim to the laurels due to him. During his operational years in India, and even more so after he had left the scene, greater and ever greater works of irrigation were planned and executed, the biggest of them in the Land of The Five Rivers, the Punjab. Those famous men, along with others equally deserving but now forgotton, who carried them out would have agreed on one thing. Arthur Cotton began it all. He was the master in whose steps they trod.

In 1835 the Government, for whatever reason, loosened the purse strings and invited Cotton to domesticate the Cauvery and the Coleroon. In the two years or so before that he had made a careful study of the river from source to sea and knew exactly what had to be done. Two anicuts were needed, the first or Upper Anicut, spanning the head of the Coleroon. This would compel the water, or part of it, to wheel right into the Cauvery while still leaving plenty for Trichinopoly on the left. Trichinopoly was one of the few Indian names known everywhere in England. Its excellent cigars ('Flor de Dindigul' was the most famous) were smoked in every pot-house and club in London. The second anicut would have to be even bigger, 70 miles downstream and forcing the Coleroon to yield up its water to supply the southern part of Arcot. Construction would be very different from the Rideau, for the beds were as dissimilar as they could be. 'Not a vestige of anything but sand to an unknown depth.' This was, of course, common knowledge and believed to be fatal to any construction work. The Cottons, Arthur and Fred alike, took another view. The anicuts could not be of solid masonry but mere surface coatings of stone over the sand of the river bed. Nor was the labour available to Cotton very much like By's Irishmen. Tamils are by nature neither of heroic stature nor outstanding natural beauty. By even greater contrast, however, they were highly intelligent and quick to learn what was needed of them. It was the Collectors' business to recruit them and there was no shortage of men anxious to earn some money.

The work was carried on at a speed which, for India of the 1830s, might fairly be called breakneck. During 1836, and within a period of six months from the plans being sanctioned, enough had been done to capture most of the water delivered by that year's monsoon, though it was perhaps lucky for the builders that it was a fairly dry season. The masonry, made up from stone quarried at a distance too great to be convenient, contained twenty-two small sluices with a permanent weir across the river at the head of Srirangam island. In the words of Lady Hope, 'So much water was stored, even at this early date from commencement, that much distress was prevented and the treasury, instead of being depleted, received additional revenue'. Being an experimental work, it could hardly have been perfect. The Triennial Review of Irrigation in India for 1918-1921 had all the advantages of a distant prospect but one must take it as factually correct: 'The sluices proved utterly inadequate and the bed of the Coleroon upstream rose gradually till it was level with the top of the work. The excess volumes passed into the Cauvery led to great erosion of the banks and deepening the bed of that branch, and threatened to make the Cauvery instead of the Coleroon the main flood-carrier of the river, with disastrous results to Tanjore. Consequently, in 1843-1845 it became necessary largely to increase the sluiceways in the Upper Anicut, to lower its crest in a considerable portion of its length, and to construct a masonry bar, known as the Cauvery dam, across the head of the Cauvery branch.' Half a loaf is generally reckoned better than no bread, and the rice-growers of the area were not ungrateful for what they had received. Over the years to come the Upper Anicut became changed out of all recognition, but it for ever retains the title of being the first of its kind.

The second anicut, a far bigger affair, was some 70 miles

downstream on the Coleroon and was begun at much the same time as the former. Once again it was necessary for the work to be rushed on during the cessation of freshes in the river and this time the builders had a stroke of good fortune. As no quarry of suitable stone could be found anywhere near the site, Cotton interested himself in the ruins of a nearby temple of great antiquity. The local Brahmins were well disposed and permitted him to carry away from the jungle in which it stood all the stone that made up its boundary wall. This was exactly what Cotton needed and the wall yielded up sufficient dressed stone for the completion of the entire work. The Collector of Tanjore did not share the economy of enthusiasm of a later Government, for he wrote to the Board of Revenue in 1838 that 'There was not an individual in the province who did not consider it (the Upper Anicut) the greatest blessing that had ever been conferred upon it (sic)', adding that 'the name of its projector would in Tanjore survive all the Europeans who had been connected with it.' Subsequent events have demonstrated that this, though hardly grammatical, was not mere hyperbole. The annual profit on the capital expended was 69% for the Upper Anicut and nearly 100% for the lower. More to the point, Cotton's first great work exorcised the spectre of famine that had for so long haunted the dreams of every farmer and family in the land. From then on, at times of famine in neighbouring districts, Cotton's parishioners were able not merely to provide for their own needs but to send great quantities of rice to their less fortunate brethren. The first call came almost at once, during the dreadful year of 1837-38. Had Cotton's work ended there he would still have deserved India's gratitude, but greater things lay ahead.

Irrigation was at last being taken seriously and Cotton's contemporary and rival, Proby Cautley, was already at work on the Doab Canal, drawn from the left bank of the Jumna far away in the Punjab. Cotton, though his reputation was made, had no part in it for several years to come. Then, in 1845, came the next challenge. The mighty River Godavari rises in the Western Ghats and flows into the Bay of Bengal near to the old French settlement of Yanam. During the early 1840s the district of Rajahmundry, at the head of its delta and some 50 miles from the sea, was in a very unhappy state. A serious famine had struck, the inhabitants were reduced to penury and the revenue in consequence was sadly in arrears. The river flowed unchecked to the sea as it had always done and the only source of water consisted of the usual tanks. Edmund Burke reckoned that throughout the Carnatic there must have been not less than 10,000 of them ranging from reservoirs to ponds. As always, the country depended entirely on the whim of whatever power sends the south-west monsoon. The Madras Government invited Arthur Cotton to see whether he could not manage affairs better. The method to be adopted could only be the same as the one that had served so well on the Cauvery, but the size of the task was bigger by far. The only possible place for the anicut was on a reach of the river some 3½ miles in width. Arthur Cotton wrote of his first contact with the business to his brother and confidant Fred. 'I asked the Board of Revenue for 6 officers, 6 or 8 sappers, and others, telling them that I was done up and could do nothing myself but look on. In answer to this I got 1 young hand to teach and 2 apprentice surveyors! With scarcely strength to ride 10 miles, I started on this expedition to turn the Godavari out of its bed and make it do something for its livelihood, a river only 7 times the breadth of the Mississippi at a spot where I am now pitched. The more I worked the stronger I became, which was well, for I had to take on, or help in, every line of level that was made, not having got one single level from my surveyors that wasn't altogether false. The site I have fixed upon for the anicut is at the head of the delta. It commands 2,000 square miles of the richest alluvial land. The river here is 6,000 yards wide including islands. The anicut would be 5,000 yards in length.'

Arthur Cotton, of course, knew all about Cautley's work and did not altogether admire it. Cautley had put his faith in temporary bunds which had to be rebuilt every year. Cotton determined upon permanent diversion works, however daunting the prospect might look. It was the existence of islands that made the thing possible. At Dowlaishwaram, 25 miles below the point where the river leaves the hills for the plains by way of a most spectacular gorge, he decided to build four weirs, connecting the three intermediate islands with the left bank and right bank, the largest having a length of nearly 5,000 feet. In all he planned for headworks comprising 2½ miles of weir, 1½ miles of embankment and canal heads leading to three separate systems, the Eastern, Central and

Western Delta. Compared with the Cauvery operations there were both advantages and otherwise. The labourers whom Cotton would have to employ were nothing like as serviceable, for the delta people were wretchedly poor and dispirited. If that were not enough, they endured malaria casualties on a scale comparable with Cranberry Swamp. The Canadian mosquito may have been the more vigorous but the Indian had far greater experience.

The other side of the account was more encouraging, and Cotton regarded the job as being technically easier than the Coleroon had been. For one thing, there was abundant raw material at hand, though much of the bill was made up of wages to those pioneers who were sent out to find it. As there could be no question of working with the sophistication of mid-Victorian engineers at home, Cotton settled for methods which his reports regularly described as 'rude'. Rough stone was easily to be had, lime of hydraulic quality turned up almost on the spot and teak, that noble wood, was there for the cutting. This last gift of nature was of critical importance, for it provided the rails of the railroad needed to carry the stone. Experiment soon showed that the long, straight logs could serve their purpose without being sawed: it was sufficient merely to flange the ends and secure them with 2″ irons screwed down hard. Cotton, in one of his regular reports, told of 'The comparatively imperfect apparatus we have used, viz, wooden rails and 2-ton cranes'. He regretted that this had to be the limit, for the anicut was made entirely from great chunks of undressed stone, some of them weighing 2 or 3 tons each. 'With wagons, rails and cranes calculated for 10 ton loads or even 5 tons it could be executed with great expedition and very cheaply. By this means of construction also what would probably be the main obstacle would be overcome without any trouble, that is the disposal of the large stream of water which flows down the river even in the hot weather; this would find its way through the open stonework while it was under construction and a lining wall along the upper face of the dam could be added afterwards.' One essential is mentioned in a letter from Captain Orr. Nothing remotely like an arch must be used; on a foundation of sand stretching down nobody knew how far the risk of subsidence at one end only could not be taken. With the ruder method if the bed sank the masonry would sink with it. The river flowed more slowly than the

Coleroon and when the gear was set up and the workers had got into the swing of it 1,000 tons of rough stone were being laid every day. It was not by anybody's choice that the work was so carried out, for Cotton had observed in his Report (dated Vizagapatam 12 August, 1844) that neither bricks nor squared stone were available. Despite all that, the primitive structure stood fast. The design was, inevitably, less than perfect since experience had to be bought and paid for. The weirs were too low and had later to be raised: the cost was greater than Cotton had bargained for and the area irrigated was less than expected. 'Great expedition' stretched out to five full years, in large part because of the climate. Those parts of southern India lying near to the coast bathe in a humidity beyond the capacity of most Europeans to endure for very long and the diseases that go with it were rife. 'Almost every one of these officers was obliged to go either to Europe or Australia after being one, two or three years in the District,' ran another part of the same report. The disruption thus caused hardly needs explaining.

The Collector, Mr Prendergast, wrote later to the Board of Finance in Madras with his opinion of what had happened. 'It is not perhaps extraordinary that the project of an anicut across the mighty stream of the Godavari, with the avowed intent of casting water over the broad extent of the Delta should find (the people) startled and incredulous and unwilling to venture their labor (sic) and capital on extending and improving their cultivation until one or two years' experience shall have shown them that the scheme is not illusory.' They ought to have been convinced. The canals served not only to irrigate great tracts of rice fields but many of them served as navigation channels. Cheap and easy transport was almost as important as agriculture itself. The Most Noble the Governor in Council — for such was the Byzantine style of head office — was certainly pleased with the work.

Cotton had always set great store by the navigation part of the business. In his report dated 10 June, 1852, he said flatly that 'The navigation of the channels formed part of the original project, and is indeed an essential part of any project for raising this neglected country to a state worthy of a civilised government.' Before handing over the task he was able to assert that about 300 miles were partly in use; the cost of transport by water of every ton of grain would, he estimated, be about 15 pence as against over a guinea by road: 'I need not say that such roads have yet to be made.' In 1890 the secretary to Lord Connemara, Governor of Madras, wrote of a water-journey undertaken by his chief and others along the canal from the sea to the dam. 'The character of the country much resembles the Fens . . . the artificial waterway grows broader and broader till, near Dowlaishweram, it becomes as wide as the Thames at Maidenhead, but probably contains a great deal more water . . . Immediately in front extends the first portion of the great Anicut which, with the help of 3 islands at the head of the Delta, holds up the river and diverts its waters on either side, so as to irrigate upwards of 612,000 acres of fertile rice-bearing lands, and to water with gold a delta of 2,000 square miles.' The secretary, Mr Rees, had enjoyed the education proper to a gentleman. 'Every river in India is a Pactolus, but this great stream has been made more subservient to the wants of man than perhaps any other of its size in the world.'

Bringing all this about nearly killed its chief architect. In 1848, after the first year, Arthur Cotton's health gave way and he went on leave to Tasmania once more. Other Madras Engineers, all of them Addiscombe-trained men, continued the work during his absence. Arthur Cotton wrote of them to his brother Fred, then busying himself with saving the forests of southern India from destruction and laying the foundations of the Indian Forest Department which came into existence some ten years later. 'I have the most excellent set of officers — 4 of them — the hardest-working fellows I ever saw. Young Haig is, I think, the most promising engineer I have known.' Cotton's demand for professional help seems at last to have been answered. The senior of them, Captain (later Major-General) Charles Orr was entrusted with building the great weir, a work in which he was later joined by Fred Cotton. Lieutenant F. H. Rundall rose in his turn to Major-General's rank, became Head of the Indian Irrigation Department and will appear again in this chronicle when it tells of the River Nile. 'Young Haig' — Felix Haig — who also ended his days as Major-General, began his career by preparing designs for making the Godavari partially navigable and completing the great dam with its attendant locks at the first barrier. With that behind him, he built the Gunnaram Aqueduct which carried one of the canals over the river into Nagaram Island. It was made up of forty-nine spans, each with 40 feet of waterway and a channel 24 feet wide. One might pause to remember the youth and lowly ranks of the men responsible for these masterpieces of the engineer's art. Only one was more than a subaltern; Cotton himself a mere Major. The fourth man, John Smith, never rose above Colonel, but he had his claims to remembrance. He was to become, first, Master of the Mint and later Chairman of the Madras Railway Company. Arthur Cotton came back in September, 1850, and resumed overall supervision of the last stages of the work. Fred joined him two years later and, when the works were completed, assumed responsibility for their future. They remained as the Cottons had left them until 1890 when two of the canal-heads had to be rebuilt. During those forty years they had served their turn. The population doubled and a district which had for so long been neglected and half starved became one of the most prosperous in India.

There were, however, still other districts which remained in the pitiable state which Tanjore and the Godavari delta had endured before the Cottons came. Probably the worst in southern India was the next Delta to the south of the Godavari, that of the Krishna, sometimes in the records called Kistna. Here the Company had no excuse for its dogged refusal to do anything, for it was half a century earlier, in 1792, that the river had been surveyed and plans drawn up for a regular irrigation scheme. The brain behind it had been that of the famous Alexander Beatson who, as Surveyor-General of Madras, had drawn up the plans for General Harris' attack on Tipu's fortress of Seringapatam. Beatson, no sapper but an officer of the Madras Infantry, had advised the building of an anicut at Bezwada, some 60 miles above the river mouth. The Government of the time had passed his plans on, not to an engineer but to an astronomer. Michael Topping, in company with a sapper officer named Caldwell (whose efforts to dam the Coleroon were to be equally unrewarded), had then spent some three years making an elaborate survey and at its conclusion announced that he was in broad agreement with Beatson's ideas. Everything was solemnly reduced into writing and sent to the Company's London headquarters in Leadenhall Street where it was equally solemnly filed. The Krishna continued to run unvexed to the sea for yet more decades and during the great — though not the greatest — famine of 1832 people died by the hundreds of thousands for want of water for their crops. Seven years later the Madras Board of Revenue, disconcerted by the shortage of income from land tax, called for yet another report. Captain Buckle of the Madras Engineers brought forward two reports, again to the effect that Beatson appeared to have got it right. The Board, as money-grubbing as ever, remained unmoved. 'Very large and costly works like the anicut at Baizwarah [the spelling of Indian place names was always more or less phonetic] are clearly inexpedient and impracticable' was its considered judgement. So matters languished until 1844 when Arthur Cotton's success in taming great rivers could hardly be longer ignored. The task of drawing up detailed plans was given to Captain Henry Atwell Lake, RE, whose education had comprehended both Harrow and Addiscombe.

In 1847 Lake took counsel with brother sappers, two of whom were experienced hands at the business. Edward Buckle was still in the service and Charles Orr had just completed his great weir across the Godavari. Naturally enough they sought the advice of the master-dammer but Arthur Cotton was enjoying one of his bouts of sickness and could do little for them. Such help as was possible he gave ungrudgingly, for Cotton lacked the smallest trace of pettiness or jealousy. To him it was both a duty and a pleasure to pass on all that experience had taught him and to make sure that, when his innings closed, there were plenty of competent hands to continue the work. Among the most notable was to be Major-General Orr. Colonel Lake achieved fame in another way.★

The Krishna anicut was as different from that of the Godavari as the Godavari had been from the Coleroon. The gorge of the river where it enters the plain is much nearer to its mouth and there is but the one stream. The new anicut would be not nearly as long as that on the Godavari but it needed to be much higher, 20 feet as against 14. The river runs swiftly between rocky hills with a width of rather less than a mile and, as always, the bed is of pure sand.

★ The defence of Kars by a Turkish garrison against Russia during the Crimean War was a feat of arms equal to that of Gordon in Khartoum. Sir William Fenwick Williams commanded, with Lake as his engineer. When, after 6 months, Kars capitulated, General Mouravieff remarked that 'Posterity will stand amazed at the endurance, the courage, and the discipline which this siege has called forth in the remains of an army'. Fenwick Williams and Lake were heroes to mid-Victorian England. Deservedly.

Only solid masonry would serve for a torrent that could rise by 40 feet when the floods came. It took four years, between 1851 and 1854, to finish it. The lion's share of the credit has to go to Charles Orr who, as Colonel Sandes says, 'completed the work successfully, rapidly, and without any serious mistakes, and so, by a system of canals on either bank, brought the blessings of irrigation to the Kistna Delta'. He certainly did that. Another 400,000 acres became reliable, life-giving rice fields. It is, perhaps, not all that remarkable that when the Great Mutiny came in 1857 the Madras Presidency stood firmly aside from it. And the work endured. In 1877 came the greatest famine known to India's recorded history. It is reckoned — though nothing of this kind can be more than a guess — that 4 million people died of starvation in the 'more or less unprotected' districts of the Presidency. In Tanjore, the Godavari and Krishna deltas not one person died. And the food they were able to send out is calculated to have saved the lives of 3 million outside their parishes.

By the Mutiny year no name stood higher in India than that of Arthur Cotton. The Madras Government recorded an opinion of some eloquence.

'If we have done our duty and have founded a system which will be a source of strength and wealth and credit to us as a nation, it is due to one master mind, which, with admirable industry and perseverance, in spite of every discouragement, has worked out this great result. Other able and devoted officers have caught Colonel Cotton's spirit, and have rendered invaluable aid under his advice and direction: but for this creation of genius we are indebted to him alone. Colonel Cotton's name will be venerated by millions yet unborn, when many who now occupy a much larger place in the public view will be forgotten: but, although it concerns not him, it would be for our own sake a matter of regret if Colonel Cotton were not to receive due acknowledgment during his own lifetime.' One may fairly ponder what the Government had in mind as 'every discouragement'. Self-criticism was never the Company's style. Cotton did, indeed, receive a knighthood — 'the reward of a provincial mayor', as Arthur Conan Doyle called it — in 1861 and a KCSI (Second Class) 5 years later. One could hardly call it being loaded with honours. Equally one may suspect that Arthur Cotton did not care a pice about it.

In spite of his indifferent health Cotton lived to the respectable age of 96. By the time the Krishna anicut was opened the greater part of his work was done, but India had neither finished with him nor he with India. One has, however, to record that the great days were over. Cotton retired from the Indian service in 1862 and, like so many old Company officers, was transferred to that of the Queen. This made no difference to his devotion to Indian affairs and his mind never turned far from the unexplored possibilities of using her rivers to great advantage, especially as water-borne highways. Undoubtedly cheap transport was one of the most pressing needs but Cotton, like those whom he had anathematized earlier, had been too long in India to be up to date. The railway and the steam locomotive were, to him, expensive luxuries far beyond India's communal pocket and his opposition to them was so uncompromising that his adversaries spoke of him as having water on the brain. This was hardly fair, as well as being unkind, for there was still room for both, at any rate for some time to come. The completion of the line from Bombay to Calcutta in 1870 proclaimed that thenceforth steam would have to be the dominant partner though canals might still have their uses in the remoter places. Cotton remained unpersuaded.

His remarkable brain produced plans for navigable canals running, roughly speaking, from Karachi to Cawnpore, Calcutta and Cuttack by way of Mangalore to Madras, a distance of some 4,000 miles in all. It could have been done. Cotton himself asserted that 'There is not a single obstacle to this and the results would be far beyond calculation'. So, inevitably, would have been the cost and at costing work of unprecedented size Arthur Cotton did not excel. Nor, for the matter of that, did anybody else. The Government had had recent nasty experiences of canal expenditure over-running estimates, one of them being the failure of the Madras Irrigation Company of which Fred Cotton had been Chief Engineer. It never gave serious thought to Arthur Cotton's, enormous project and it was probably right. For some little while his pedestal rocked slightly. Then came the great dispute with Proby Cautley — another Addiscombe man, but a gunner — over the Ganges Canal. Cotton, the sand expert, reckoned the head of it to have been put in the wrong place. Cautley had put it at a point where the river, on leaving the mountains, had a shingle bed and a high incline. Cotton was of opinion that a better place would have been much lower down, even though this would have meant building on sand and much excavation. After the work had been completed and much money spent an investigation came to the conclusion that Cotton had been right all along and much rebuilding followed.

In 1877, coincidentally the year of the Great Famine, Cotton went home and settled at Dorking. Within a year he was called upon to testify before the House of Commons Committee on the subject of the public works India needed in consequence of these most recent horrors. Cotton's experience followed that of Colonel By. The members, probably enjoying the chance to bait a General — Cotton had been promoted Major-General on retirement — were rude and hostile. Their report, in his view, demonstrated how completely they had failed to grasp even the most obvious matters relating to irrigation and cheap transport. This can hardly have surprised him. It took until 1900, a year after Cotton's death, for the then Viceroy, Lord Curzon, to tell the Legislative Assembly at Simla that Cotton had been right and the Honourable Members wrong.

India did not need to be told of how great were Arthur Cotton's services to her. As already said, she has honoured him as she has honoured no other Englishman. And in so doing India brought honour to herself.

Nor did India's generous appreciation of Cotton's work and character end with the putting up of a statue. On 15 May, 1989, the Institution of Engineers met in Hyderabad to celebrate Sir Arthur's birthday — he would have been 187 — and to hear their Chairman announce that this would henceforth be a regular affair. In the words of Mr. Hanumantha Rao, it would be done in order 'to infuse enthusiasm among young engineers to achieve greater heights in their chosen fields of activity'. It could not have been better expressed.

VI

Paente Ubique
The Exploits of Major-General Henry Spencer Palmer

THE BUSINESS OF MILITARY ENGINEERING as
carried out by the alumni of Woolwich and Addiscombe was always
something of a family affair. Admiral Sir John Fisher once went
on record as saying that nepotism is the secret of efficiency. And
he was quite right. In 1838, while Arthur Cotton was at grips with
the first of his anicuts, the next generation was being made ready
in nearby Bangalore. Jane Palmer, wife to Colonel John Freke
Palmer of the Company's service, presented him with a son on
30 April. His sapper credentials could hardly have been bettered,
for his mother's brother was Lieutenant — in due time
Lieutenant-General Sir — Henry James, already an officer of the
Ordnance Survey of which he was to become the most renowned
of all the Directors-General. The boy, christened Henry Spencer,
showed early signs of something uncomfortably like genius. In
accordance with custom he was packed off home early and sent to
a school in Bath. At the age of 17 he passed out seventh in a batch
of forty at a public competition for entrance to The Shop, being by
a long way the youngest candidate. Uncle Henry had passed out
from the same establishment thirty years earlier. Both Palmers and
James came of what were called good family. It would be a great
mistake to think, as some do, of the Royal Engineers being officered
by brainy nobodies.

On leaving Woolwich young Palmer performed the usual stint
with his uncle's Ordnance Survey but, at just 20, he had a stroke
of unusual good fortune. It came about in this way. Nobody set
much store by the Pacific side of Canada, for it was a long distance

from everywhere and seemed to have nothing much to reward any possible settlers. All of a sudden, in June, 1858, news reached California that gold had been struck there a couple of months earlier. The remnant of forty-niners and other opportunists promptly moved north. Within a few months some 50,000 of them were camped on Vancouver Island and something had to be done about it. In August 1858, a great tract of the mainland, vaguely defined, was nominated a Colony under the name of British Columbia. Up till then it had commonly been called New Caledonia, a noble name that became degraded to that of an obscure French penal settlement in the South Seas. The Island, one of Captain Cook's many discoveries, was undeniably British, for it had been ceded by the occupying power, Spain, after the Nootka Sound affair in 1790; since 1849 it had been a full-blown Colony with Victoria for its capital. The hinterland belonged, if it belonged to anyone, to the North West Company founded by the explorers Alexander Mackenzie, Simon Fraser and David Thompson and merged in 1821 with the Hudson's Bay Company. After the merger a number of traders had moved in but there was still no settled population to speak of. Away to the North lay Russian Alaska but the Czar of All the Russias, so soon after the Crimean War, was more interested in the golden road to Samarkand than in furs and fish. The great tracts of forest and mountain between the Rockies and the Ocean remained inviolate. In such a place the miners would be a law to themselves and such could not be tolerated. As recently as 1854 there had been the painful experience in Australia of the Eureka Stockade, the Californian Rangers Revolver Brigade, and a short-lived Miners Republic. A repetition of this in the new Colony could not be allowed to happen. All the same, the Army was fully stretched throughout the Empire and to find a substantial garrison was not possible. One course remained. The Royal Engineers were trained soldiers and could take care of any number of rugged individualists. Unlike other troops, they could also help to tame a wilderness. By a happy accident there was already a small party in the Colony. It had been as long ago as 1818 that Britain and the United States had agreed by solemn treaty that the boundary between them should be the 49th parallel of latitude. The Treaty, however, only took notice of those parts to the east of the Rocky Mountains and as a strict matter of law the Americans were at liberty to push up to the Columbia River. By the 1846 Treaty, however, the parallel was agreed as the international frontier along its entire length to the Pacific. It looked neat on a map; on the ground it meant nothing save to a well-equipped surveyor. It was the gold that brought matters to a head. With everybody minded to make his fortune digging away at the gravel bars of the Fraser River something had to be done to demonstrate on the ground whose writ ran where. In June, 1858, the US Boundary Commission arrived in Victoria: the British party, six officers and fifty-six other ranks of the Royal Engineers, sailed in in mid-July after a long and disagreeable voyage. The secretary was Lieutenant Charles Wilson, RE, his first of many appearances on the international stage. The miners had been at work for some three months. Wilson noted that they had already sent down 8,000 ounces and the mines were expected at least to equal those of California. In their social behaviour they were already anticipating Robert W. Service.

The task of the two Commissions was to agree exactly where the parallel ran and to cut out a swathe through the forest, plain for all to see. At specified distances it would be marked out with iron posts whose positions would be final for all time. It did not sound easy work, nor was it. Much of the difficulty came from constant inability to agree on small calculations. It was not the hard-faced Yankee trying to do down the cunning Limey, or vice-versa. The ill-feeling went back to antiquity, for the American Commissioner was a Campbell and the British a Douglas. The fact that he had been born in British Guiana of a Creole mother made him scotcher than Sir Walter. Between the two stood an Englishman with a name that recalled Drake and Queen Elizabeth, Major Hawkins, RE, commander of the British end of the business. As time went by they seem to have got on better, probably because they had little choice. Rumours of Indian uprisings, provoked by miners taking over their land, were never quiet for long.

The Boundary Commission sappers were a body quite distinct from the British Columbia Detachment which arrived in four ships late in 1858 and early in 1859. Their commander, Colonel Richard Clement Moody, RE, walked down the gangway on Christmas Day, 1858. At the age of 45 he already had a considerable record of service behind him. On the strictly engineering side, he had been Professor of Fortification at The Shop and in that capacity had been responsible for planning the restoration of Edinburgh Castle. So excellent was his work reckoned that both the Queen and the Prince Consort had commanded his attendance in order to be congratulated. On the rougher side of service life, he had been first Governor of the Falkland Islands between 1842 and 1848, at a time when all his qualities of hardihood and personal courage had been required in full. Plainly he had been as good a Governor as he had been a designer of castles. The Falklands, in Moody's time, had been reckoned unruly. When Lord Charles Beresford, senior midshipman of HM corvette *Clio*, visited them in 1864 he found the population to be almost entirely made up of ex-Royal Marines and their families. The man who had made such a transformation for the better of a distant colony was just what the Government needed. Colonel Moody (the 'Moody's Brook' that cropped up so often in news bulletins during the Falklands war was named for him) was duly appointed Lieutenant-Governor and Chief Commissioner of Lands and Works in British Columbia. Among the five sapper officers accompanying him, each hand-picked by Moody himself, was Lieutenant Henry Spencer Palmer. The 'other ranks', as the British Army has always quaintly called those who do not hold commissions, numbered 150 and included every kind of tradesman needed for setting up a new country. There were carpenters and printers, surveyors and explosive experts, mapmakers and bakers; many of them could double or treble their skills at a pinch. 150 men do not seem too many for the business of siting towns and laying them out, making the roads and bridges to connect them, surveying the great unsurveyed and, incidentally, keeping the Queen's Peace as trained soldiers whenever called upon to do so.

If trade follows the flag the flag follows gold, and at a brisker pace. Victoria, at the southern tip of Vancouver Island, had come into existence during the busy year of '49 and its raison d'etre was the fur trade. It was the private domain of the Hudson's Bay Company whose Charter dating from 1670 was only a few decades younger than that of the East India adventurers. By 1857 the population had increased to about 400 and its ruler, Mr Douglas, was also Chief Factor of the Company, Agent of the Puget's Sound Agricultural Company and, more recently, Governor of the Colony of Vancouver Island. He had the rare experience of seeing a gold rush begin. It was during morning service on a Sunday in April, 1858. The side-wheeler *Commodore,* flying the Stars and Stripes, steamed into the harbour and disembarked 450 rough-looking men, more than one to every British inhabitant. It says much for Sapper discipline that not a single one of its men left his duty to join them and make his fortune. Instead they established their quarters on the mainland and set about cutting vistas through the trees eastward from Point Roberts, where the parallel falls into the ocean. Most of the miners also left the island and headed up the Fraser where gold could still be extracted by the simplest methods of digging and panning. The tent city of Victoria gradually emptied.

It has been mentioned before that until very recently the part of the Canadian mainland between the Rockies and the ocean had been commonly called, when it was necessary for it to be called anything, New Caledonia. This was not without reason for, quite apart from the Campbells and Douglases, the Hudson's Bay Company seemed to be run entirely by Highlanders. They were, taken in the round, of a superior kind to the civilians of the East India Company and were probably more at home in another land of mountain and flood than would have been most of the English. It was they who had set up the forts — a 1914 map shows 132 of them — where Indians came to exchange their furs for trade goods. The accidents of history had also put quite a number of their kinsmen into the American camp and there was no great love lost between them. The British government was uneasy because at any moment the Americans might announce that their people were in danger from the Indians and move troops in. Once there they would have been hard to dislodge. In fact America in 1859 was far more interested in colonizing Kansas and Nebraska than New Caledonia. Nobody, before the Presidential campaign of 1860, gave much thought to the possibility of the States tearing themselves in two. Nevertheless the two sides got across each other in a way that came dangerously near to a little local war.

The cause of it all was a pig, resident on the island of San Juan de Fuca. For complicated reasons, unnecessary to be told here, the island had been left out of the Oregon Treaty. Both sides staked claims. Douglas set up a Company farm. The US authorities threw the island open to squatters. One such was named Lyman A.

Cutler. On a day in June, 1859, he remarked a pig, unknown to him, rootling in his potato patch. Being a man of swift decision, Mr Cutler shot it. Too late he learned that he had bagged no common porker but a Company pig. Had it only had a name the animal might have earned the immortality of Captain Jenkins of the Ear, for retribution followed the outrage. The Company delivered a bill for $100, which seems large. It did not, however, justify Brigadier-General Harney, by common consent the most unpleasant man in the US officer corps, sending not a cheque but an infantry company. Its commander, George Pickett, was a Virginian gentleman of very different quality. Gettysburg and Five Forks were waiting for him and his name has a secure place in his country's history. For the moment, however, Pickett was caught up in farce rather than tragedy. Governor Douglas, in best Palmerston style, sent HMS *Plumper,* the next best thing to a gunboat. On board, as honorary marines, were Colonel Moody, RE, and fourteen sappers. In fine summer weather the two sides contented themselves with pulling faces at each other until the arrival of General Winfield Scott who promptly removed Brigadier-General Harney. The matters at issue were then discussed amiably enough and the future of the island was left to be determined by the German Emperor as arbitrator. It took him until 1872 to give his award. The hostility of England during his war with France could now be punished, if only lightly. The island went to the United States. Whether they settled up for the pig is uncertain.

Colonel Moody was the Governor's man for all seasons. The Pig War had hardly ended before another conflict erupted. Ned McGowan has had a bad press. If, as seems probable, he was a scoundrel, he did at least bring some style to the profession. Earlier in his career he had been a member of the Philadelphia legislature but one lapse had been too much even for so easy-going a body. Ned McGowan had been made Superintendent of Police. When subordinates found that a bank robbery had been carried out by their Chief it was time for him to go. He went to California as a genuine forty-niner but, possessing talents that should not be wasted, he became a Judge. What malfeasance brought his judicial career to an end is mysterious, for it was never investigated. Ned, in the nick of time, jumped a ship bound for the Fraser River diggings. There, by force of character and experience, he soon

111

became the first man in Hill's Bar, a substantial gold-diggers' camp. Once installed, McGowan picked a quarrel with the neighbouring magistrate at Fort Yale. Captain, as he styled himself, Whannell had reached his position in much the same fashion as Ned McGowan, though his starting point had been in Australia. The upshot of this was something like a miners' rebellion, on the lines of the Eureka Stockade of 1853. The threat to a settled rule of law was too strong to be ignored. Colonel Moody and his sappers, the only formed military body in the Colony, represented authority and set out to make it respected. Judge Begbie, son to a Colonel of Royal Engineers, a handful of Royal Marines and the crew of HMS *Plumper* set out up-river, guided by some Hudson's Bay Company men. When they reached Hill's Bar, having picked up various auxiliaries on the way, they were confronted by an armed mob. The sailors performed Royal Tournament exercises with their field-gun, the sappers plainly meant business and the rebellion evaporated. A moment of high drama ended with a Church service conducted by Colonel Moody, followed by drinks all round provided by McGowan. Moody, in his famous letter to Arthur Blackwood, lamented that no good young parsons would stir themselves to leave home and take up cures amongst 'such fine fellows as these miners'.

It was not only curates that the colony lacked. Once again the chronicler is Colonel Moody. He wrote enthusiastically about the gold strikes, adding, 'It seems to us incredible that people from home do not come out, and this is attributed to the influence of the American press who do all they can to run it down, while Americans at the same time are literally streaming into it. It will be an American country before long, if not neutralised by the presence of many Englishmen coming out at once'.

The relations between Britain and America in the years before the Civil War were much the same as they have always been, equally compounded of suspicion, jealousy and a grudging knowledge that neither had any friend anywhere save the other. None of the other Powers of the day particularly liked either of them, nor had they cause to. Russia had withdrawn behind her forests, the Austrian Empire was digesting its revolutions and having a small war with France in North Italy. Germany did not exist, but Bismarck did and his work had begun. Napoleon III seemed to weathercock between amity and enmity; as he built his harbour at Cherbourg, Lord Palmerston built his forts opposite it. To confuse matters even further it was an army of both British and French infantry that, at almost exactly the same time, was teaching the Manchu Emperor that crime does not pay by systematically wrecking his Summer Palace. This hardly warranted oaths of eternal friendship between the two nations. Lord Tennyson called poetically for riflemen to form, and they did. Mr Punch, though never Laureate, did better with some more or less deathless verse:

'Oh, Jonathan, dear Jonathan, a wretched world we see,
There's scarce a freeman in it now excepting you and me.'

After expressing an unfavourable opinion of the way in which Europe had degenerated into military dictatorships, the verses ended with:

'They hate us, brother Jonathan, these tyrants; they detest,
The island sons of liberty and freemen of the west,
It angers them that we survive their savage will to stem,
A sign of hope unto their slaves — a sign of fear to them.'

There may have been something in it. At about the same time that Moody's sappers were setting out to take order with Ned McGowan, Admiral Hope, pressing the luck of the Navy a little too hard, attacked the Chinese forts at the mouth of the Pei-ho River with his gunboats. One of them, HMS *Plover*, came under heavier fire than she had bargained for and all but nine of her forty crew were hit. In navy fashion they stuck to their guns though the position was hopeless. Watching them from the quarterdeck of USS *Toeywhan* stood Commodore Joseph Tattnall, puffing quietly on his cigar. He had no call to love the Limeys. As a midshipman he had fought against them in 1812. All the same, as he was to report to his Navy Board, 'Blood is thicker than water'. He sent in his launch to help rescue the wounded. On its return he noticed several of his own men smoke-blackened. To his 'What have you been doing, you rascals?' came the answer, 'Beg pardon, sir, but they were a bit short-handed with the bow gun.' The Board in Washington made no complaint. Touching though all this was, it did not alter the fact that nature abhors a vacuum and British Columbia was one.

Colonel Moody had not been sent there for pig and bar-room

wars but to set up the pattern of a new country. One of its first needs would be a capital city and it was up to the sappers to provide one. Moody had begun his venture into the interior in January, 1859, by remarking that the entrance to the Fraser presented no difficulty so long as steam tugs were available. There were precious few British ones. 'At present our American friends run away with everything, small blame to them if the English won't come,' he wrote in his long letter to Mr Blackwood at the Colonial Office. Captain George Richards RN, of HM steam-sloop *Plumper* — not to be confused with Colonel By's *Pumper* — provided the means of crossing to the mainland. Moody was captivated by what he saw, comparing it not unfavourably to the Holland painted by Albert Cuyp. After steaming 20 miles up the clock-calm waters of the Fraser River — 'such a name! The proper one is Tatouche' — he found the place upon which his capital should stand. 'It is a most important spot. It is positively marvellous how singularly it is formed for the site of a large town (not a small one) to be defended against any foreign aggression.' He went on to explain how such defences should be built and spoke of the urgency of it all. 'No time should be lost in adopting the site. In a few months it may be too late.' The attractions were more than its inexpugnability. 'The site is not only convenient in every respect but it is agreeable and striking in aspect. Viewed from the Gulf of Georgia across the meadows on entering the Frazer (Moody always used this spelling), the far distant giant mountains forming a dark background, the City would appear throned Queen-like and shining in the glory of the mid-day sun. The comparison is so obvious that afterwards all hands on board the *Plumper* and indeed everyone joins in thinking the appropriate name would be "Queenborough". We all thought for a time of "Alexandrina", Victoria being already engaged for the Capital of Vancouver's Island (paltry place in comparison) but it sounds so long. I don't dislike it, however . . . The Governor very properly however says it is his intention to take instructions from Home about the Name and hopes Her Majesty may be induced to name it. I trust it will be some Royal word, stamping the country as our beloved Queen's own land. A standard for her loving subjects in this distant corner of the earth. A mark to our neighbour over the frontier that the Queen's sceptre extends here. God bless her. Americans flood us and give names in all directions.' With remarkable swiftness Her Majesty announced her pleasure. On 20 July, 1859, it was proclaimed that the name should be New Westminster. Before the name came the founders. On 12 April, 1859, the ship *Thames City* carrying the greater part of the Columbia Detachment ran slowly into Esquimalt Harbour, turned into the west wind and dropped anchor. She carried three RE officers, a surgeon and 188 sappers of all trades. Among their number was Lieutenant Henry Spencer Palmer.

The first business of the Detachment was to clear the site of New Westminster. It may have looked like a Cuyp picture from the deck of a ship but Holland does not abound with mountains and forests. The capital was, so far, not even a clearing. When Palmer caught his first sight of the place it was nothing but trees, some standing, some lying and others consumed by fire. Dotted about were a few huts, sheds and tents. The inhabitants were, in the main, mosquitoes. The newly-appointed chaplain, Mr Sheepshanks, came on the scene a little later on and was not captivated. 'On turning a corner of the river, after an hour or two of steady steaming up stream at about 15 miles from the river, the captain, who was standing by my side, said "There sir, that is your place." It was 'a bit of a clearing in a dense forest' running up-river for about a quarter of a mile and holding, he guessed, about 250 souls for his cure. Moody himself had prepared plans of what was to rise upon it while Captain Grant oversaw the work of tree removal. The combination of a military role with that of civil engineers was something new in sapper experience. When the Corps undertook the Ordnance Survey of Ireland it had been on the strict understanding that the Sappers would on no account be used for anything in the way of peace-keeping. Governor Douglas, who ran his Colony with all the heavy-handedness of a Highland chieftain, had no time for democracy or any nonsense about civil rights. His ship was going to be a tight one and his soldiers were there above all things to keep order.

The fact remained that they had order of another kind to bring to an empty land. Apart from the new towns, the crying need was for communications and Moody distributed duties among his handful of experts according to their particular skills. He had no illusions about the size of the task before him and soon reported that his small detachment could do no more than the necessary surveying and providing expert assistance to others. Palmer, whose particular bent was for exploration and mapping, was charged with the opening up of communications with the interior, first for pack and them for wheels. It was the gold that would pay the cost of the expedition and the miners must have their roads as a first priority. Mr Douglas had decided that the first one to be made should run from Harrison to Lillooet, work on which had already been started but was halted for want of competent surveyors. This absorbed most of the sappers' energies during 1859, the McGowan business causing only a tiresome interruption. Lieutenant Palmer was packed off early in May to find out what existed already in the shape of old Indian trails between the new settlement of Douglas and the Lake Lillooet. This was difficult country but in the course of the next two months Palmer concluded that the job could be done given enough labour. By the end of that summer something like 100 sappers were at work on making the trail passable for wagons. Palmer did not remain long with them. Instead of supervising the carrying out of his plans he was sent off once more into the wilds, this time to hack out a trail from New Westminster to Burrard's Inlet, a straight North to South track from the capital to the sea. This he did extremely well and his obvious skill in such matters attracted attention. Palmer's road, completed in 1861, still remains, now under the name of the North Road. Once again the construction work was left to others and Palmer returned with his theodolite, sextant and field books through the canyons of the Fraser River to Lillooet Lake. The site of Lillooet township was, meanwhile, being laid out by Corporal Duffy, RE, who was suddenly taken off his work by the Governor in person. Mr Douglas wanted some exploration done in order to ascertain the best route for the Second Portage. Duffy volunteered. His report and plans, including the making of a zig-zag wagon trail down a drop of 1,000 feet were models of excellence. Even the lower non-commissioned ranks of the RE were capable — no doubt they still are — of doing the work one associates with expensive civil engineers. His reward was to be charged with disobeying orders and losing his stripes. Sapper Duffy, however, has his memorial. He froze to death on the trail he had reconnoitred a few months later during the cruellest January anybody could remember and every available Sapper turned out to carry him to his grave in New Westminster. So intense was the cold that work had to be abandoned and all hands returned to barracks in New Westminster until the worst was over. The Hudson's Bay Company officers enlivened the tedium for some of those caught out in the hinterland with 'innumerable Scotch reels, Highland flings and Mr Macdonald (in charge of the HBC fort) gave us a capital sword dance and we then had an amateur Indian war dance and song'. Thus wrote Charles Wilson, the Secretary to the Boundary Commission, at Fort Colville. The horrors of peace also have their chroniclers. The year of 1860 was to be a good one for Palmer. In the first place there came to the Colony reinforcements for the Church, Archdeacon Wright, his wife and their pretty daughter. Henry Palmer and Mary Wright seem to have taken to each other from their first acquaintance. Then came the great work of the Columbia Detachment, the building of the Cariboo Road. The supply of gold in the bars of the Fraser River was running out when a new strike was made at Rock Creek, far to the east and almost on top of the 49th parallel. From Hope, then a sizeable village, to Rock Creek along the Similkameen River was a matter of about 75 miles. Palmer was given the task of exploring it and finding where a reasonable trail could be made which did not touch US territory. It was a nightmare road, over Manson's Mountain where he found the skeletons of sixty or seventy horses. They were one of the Hudson's Bay Company fur brigades, caught in a blizzard a few years before. As the trail led through Fort Colville, where the Boundary Commission men of both nationalities were at work, it seemed unlikely that the Americans could not know all about the new discovery. Fortunately for everybody a new and better one far away soon caused a loss of interest in Rock Creek.

Miners, in the nature of things, do not advertise their discoveries but they can never be kept secret for long. It was at some date in 1860 that two prospectors, 'Doc' Keithley and George Weaver, struck pay dirt in the tributary of the Cariboo they called Keithley Creek. It was not the easy mining of the Fraser bars, for the gold of the Cariboo lay some 40 or 50 feet below ground. This put mining out of the reach of the sieve and shovel men, for expensive gear like pumps, waterwheels and hoists had to be got into position somehow. As month followed month more strikes were made and the miners once more flocked in, accompanied by the usual camp-followers. When news of the finds at William's Creek, bigger than all the others put together, appeared in *The Times* London became interested. There had long been complaints that the sappers, useful and popular though they were, constituted a luxury the young colony could not afford. William's Creek might well pay for them. But first of all a road, not a mere pack-trail, had to be built and built, for part of the way, through the canyons of the Fraser. In other words, it must run along a ledge gouged out of the sides of sheer cliffs and, where that was not possible, it must be built out on shelves over the gaps. This was nothing new to the Royal Engineers for such were fairly common on the Indian frontier. Knowledge was not enough; there were limits to what 150 men could do.

It was not so much the length of the Cariboo Road, for it ran no more than 100 miles, as its engineering difficulties that posed the challenge. It was fortunate for the Colony that it had on hand a sufficiency of civilian contractors to carry out the donkey work and men of the quality of Walter Moberley, Joseph Trutch, Edgar Dewdney and half-a-dozen others have their place in history. The road, as finally planned by Moody, went from Yale to Lytton alongside the river and the builders, civil or military, were given specific lengths of it on which to work. It demanded a lot of manpower. The contractors at one time were advertising for 1,000 men to work on one section alone.

The Bishop did the rounds of his flock as a good shepherd ought and left some record of it. On a day in the summer of 1861, just as the Confederate guns were opening on Fort Sumpter, his journey along the Fraser brought him to its confluence with the Thompson around Lytton. Having crossed the ferry, he 'ascended to a great height on the almost perpendicular side of the mountain, on which a false step would precipitate anyone to destruction'. Conversation with a gloomy teamster who had just lost a mule over the edge did little to hearten him but 'Captain Grant and Lieutenant Palmer received us with their usual courteous hospitality. They dine at the same time with the men, so we sat down at their midday meal and enjoyed a hearty repast. It is interesting to see the wonderful change produced in a country by roads.' Grant was, by common consent, the great road-building expert. He commanded the sapper detachment which, with civilian labour to thicken them up, would take on the most difficult part of it, the southernmost reach from Yale to Chapman's Bar. The contractors would take it on to Lytton with RE advice and help available when they wanted it. Palmer served as his deputy. For a 6-mile stretch they had fifty-three sappers, hardly an excessive number for all the blasting through solid rock and subsequent cribbing that would have to be done. The Bishop, dutiful as ever, came across them in June, 1862, hard by 'the formidable mountain called the Jackass, from the propensity of mules to fall over and be lost upon its dangerous and steep pathways. The especial difficulty now was the blasting operations of the roadmakers, high up on the mountain side, from which came down, with tremendous force and fury, whole avalanches of rocks and smaller debris, shooting over and past the trail and utterly blotting it out.' Having decided to take the lower route and losing his way, the Bishop found himself 'in most imminent danger. The narrow pathway on which 10 horses (7 of them bearing packs) and 6 men were now standing, had not in some portions of it, 10 inches of footing. Above was the perpendicular mountain and below was a chasm down to the torrent, some 800 feet. What was to be done?'. Being a sensible man, he prayed. The horses were turned round, they continued their journey and 'camped in a sweet spot'. On his next visit, three months later, 'As I arrived on a small bridge over a chasm, an explosion took place immediately beneath my feet. I was enveloped in smoke, and debris was scattered around and over me . . . on passing round about 30 yards I found the blasters in a place of safety, they having fled after firing the fuse . . . They were not a little surprised to see me.'

It was in the summer of 1862 that Palmer was taken from blasting roads to go on an expedition into the practically unkown. Though not of outstanding importance in itself, it was to produce the main story about this distinguished officer on which generations of sappers have dined out. This was the way of it. The road to the Cariboo was as important to British Columbia as was the Nile to Egypt. The great wagon road from Yale was coming on slowly and painfully. It was surely only sensible to find out whether there might not be a better way further to the north, running due east from the sea at Bentinck Arm, up the Bella Coola Valley and across to William's Lake. Palmer, a very experienced hand at 23, was bidden to go and find out. Alexander Mckenzie had travelled the course long ago but there was no man then living who could give him much of an idea of what awaited the party.

Before they set off it might not come amiss to have a look at them and their equipment. The soldiers, Palmer himself and Sappers Edwards and Breakenridge, were properly dressed, though they might not have stood inspection by the Duke of Cambridge. Redcoats, since Wolfe's day, have been as much part of the Canadian scene as of the English. The fine picture by Rex Woods called 'Cariboo Road', however, probably represents engineers at work as accurately as Caton Woodville and Verestchagin did cavalry charges. They look rather too beautiful to be true. Charles Wilson, on one of his Boundary Commission forays, wrote to his sister of 'my kit consisting of a buffalo robe and roll of bacon tied up behind the saddle and my gun in front, my dress moccasins, leather trousers, ditto coat, a flannel shirt and a very old hat'. Mayne, the sailor, brought to it a touch of the Eighth Army. His corduroy trousers, so he said, were tied under the knee 'to take the drag off it when they are wet'. He tells also of the kind of rations usually carried: 'Bacon and dampers, with tea and coffee.' Columbian dampers seem to have been made to much the same recipe as the Australian variety. Mayne calls them 'cakes of dough rolled out to the size of a plate and one or two inches thick. They are cooked either by being baked in the wood ashes of the fire, or fried in the pan with bacon fat.' Sometimes they were enriched by a passenger, usually grouse. There are many good photographs of the Boundary Commission at work, including one of the young Wilson dressed as he himself described. There is also an excellent posed one of Henry Palmer. To his credit, he seems to have resisted the temptation to which Colonel Moody and others fell of growing a great sweep's brush of a beard. His moustache and whiskers are entirely what one would expect of a mid-Victorian officer and gentleman.

Early in July, 1862, Palmer and his party embarked in the steamer *Enterprise* at New Westminster bound for the North Bentinck arm. The view from the ship on arrival was not encouraging, 'snowy peaks, pine-clad slopes, rugged cliffs and precipices, naked, shapeless masses of trappean and granitic rocks projecting upwards to vast heights, gloomy valleys and picturesque waterfalls; these, in constant succession, form an aggregate of sublime and wild, though strangely desolate and unattractive scenery.' It was not until the party had moved out a little from the shore that another unattractive feature presented itself, 'low marshes and damp, steaming ground (the temperature was in the 50's) which encourages a dense growth of the penax horrida'. Nor was he captivated by the inhabitants. 'The Bella Coolas are degraded specimens of the Red Indian . . . Vices at which civilized men shudder are of frequent occurrence amongst them. Thieving is an art that all attain to perfection.' Possibly their diet had something to do with it: fresh salmon with raspberries and strawberries in summer: dried salmon with berries in winter. The salmon, as Palmer was soon to learn, were sacred as any cow to the Hindu. The Bella Coolas could also be dangerous: in 1865 they were to murder Moody's friend Mr Ogilvy. There was a price to be paid for a salmon diet. During Palmer's time with them an epidemic of smallpox, Europe's gift to many simple people, was steadily wiping them out.

Palmer mustered his party of Sappers Edwards and Breakenridge, Lieut.-Col. Foster of the police, a packer and eight horses: on 9 July they set out along the bank of the Nookhalk River heading towards the mountains. As he put it in his report, 'It would be tedious to describe at length the various obstacles that opposed our progress and the sundry shifts to which we were put in prosecuting our difficult journey.' He wrote of swamps and waterfalls, of 'magnificent mountains and clusters of mountains' and the poor quality of a soil that could grow nothing worth growing. He told of the Great Slide and of The Precipice, 'blocks of columnar basalt in the shape of multi-angular prisma averaging in their perfect state about 2 cubic feet in size . . . fitted together as perfectly as if by human agency' and of 'abrupt columnar masses of as much as 50 feet in height, which, viewed from a short distance, almost assume the appearance of massive artificial and battlemented structures.' He told of lakes, swamps and marshes, of the absence of nearly all animal life, of forests devastated by fires and of others already rotted away. He was eloquent about another aspect of the land. 'The swamps give rise to the existence of myriads of mosquitoes, the travellers' most inveterate enemy. They, with the small, black blood-sucking flies, prevail in greater or less abundance during the summer months, the whole way from the Slide to Alexander, the coldness of the nights in no way appearing to hinder their existence, and, in the worst places, they can only be described as forming a dense, living cloud which covers the country to a height of 20 feet from the ground.' The party reached Fort Alexander on the Fraser River on 13 August with one meal left in their saddle-bags.

Apart from exact astronomical observations and a report running to thirty pages, Palmer left a piece of British Columbian history behind him. All his report says comes in the admirably laconic remark that the first 57 miles from North Bentinck Arm 'owing to bad weather, trouble with the natives (which on one occasion nearly cost us our lives) and the difficulties of advancing, had occupied 18 days'. What actually happened was told later on by Sapper Edwards. They had, it seems, caught a salmon, cut it into steaks and were frying it for breakfast along with their dampers. Twice Palmer had his arm jogged and the frying-pan capsized. The second time it happened he jumped up and caught an Indian boy who appeared to have been the cause of it all. Palmer clumped his ear and let him go. As the party finished its refection Edwards called out that they were surrounded by Indians, all of them armed. Palmer very intelligently staged a distraction. His red coat and gold-laced cap were objects of desire to any Indian and it was essential to interest them in something other than murder. Waving his cap like a Salvation Army tambourine, Lieutenant Palmer performed a spirited and unaccompanied pas seul. It drew an immediate and appreciative audience. In between steps the dancer called out in Chinook an enquiry to the chiefs as to what they wanted. They announced firmly that by cutting the salmon's backbone the engineers had grievously offended the god: he would revenge himself by sending no more to the river and could be placated only by the death of the guilty. To this Palmer was more than equal. Queen Victoria, he explained, was superior in every way to any local deity and he was to her a personal friend. It only needed a word from the Sappers and the Queen would double the usual supply. This assertion was received with something like a standing ovation. A man with such powers should surely become a local resident: possibly even Mayor. To make the proposal irresistible the Chief went away, only to return with his two daughters whom he offered on permanent loan. Palmer expressed himself enchanted but was unable to take advantage of the offer before consulting his Queen who regulated such matters. The Indians, now in high good humour, took his point and agreed that the girls be returned to store pending Royal approval. They parted with expressions of goodwill all round. The reticence of Palmer's report is understandable. It would certainly be made public and Archdeacon Wright might not be amused. Archdeacons in the 1860s were still, as often as not, much like Trollope's Dr. Grantley. And daughters were still obedient. On the strictly engineering side the report was quite firm. A road to the Cariboo from the sea and over the Cascades was possible, but pointless. The existing wagon road along the Fraser promised far better. There was no arguing against this. Ten years or so later the track was examined again by Marcus Smith as a possible route for the Canadian Pacific Railway; he came to the same conclusion and the railway in its turn followed the river.

With this task completed, Palmer went back to the hard slog of road-building, this time in charge of a 9-mile stretch along the Thompson River from Lytton to Cook's Ferry. Before long the ferry went out of business and the place became Spence's Bridge. Another bridge furnished Palmer with his last task in the Colony. Mr — later Sir — Joseph Trutch had built a fine one across the Fraser above Yale at his own expense. Its opening more or less coincided with the marriage of the Prince of Wales and his Danish princess. Alexandra Bridge it became. Lieutenant Palmer, aged 23, was called upon to certify its fitness for the public service, since Mr Trutch would have to rely on tolls in order to make anything out of his investment. Palmer should have experienced no great difficulty for the suspension bridge was as strong as it was handsome. It remained in service until the coming of the railway.

The argument had been raging for some time about whether the Sappers — the 'very dear soldiers' they were called — had not outlived their usefulness. When the Confederate guns set about Fort Sumpter on 12 April, 1861, all the threats from America died. It certainly revived later in the war, over the Alabama affair and the seizure of two Confederate envoys from a British ship, but Mr Lincoln had sensibly said that one war at a time was enough. The Colony was taking shape, contractors were at work everywhere and the Queen's Peace was being maintained without military help. In 1863 the Columbia Detachment was disbanded. Only twenty-two of the party returned to England, most of them being officers with careers to pursue. The remainder settled down to becoming good Canadians. Colonel Moody, newly appointed CRE at Chatham, took his numerous family with him. They mustered a total of fourteen children. His sojourn in British Columbia is forever recalled by Moody's Inlet. That of his enemy Governor Douglas is perpetuated not merely by place names little known in the outside world but by a particularly large fir tree. Lieutenant Palmer (who had a small lake named after him) went home also, but not alone. On 7 October, 1863, at the sapper-built church of New Westminster, Mary Jane Wright became Mrs Henry Palmer. As recently as 1930, after nearly 40 years of widowhood, she was able to tell a reporter of the windy day, 'when we and the colony were both young', that sent her veil flying, of the arrival of the bridal party in a covered wagon and of the smartly turned-out escort from her husband's Corps. It was to be a very happy marriage.

After a brief honeymoon the Palmers left British Columbia for ever on 11 November, 1863, the last of the Sapper contingent to go. Though nothing like as spectacular as Cotton's anicuts, the tangible evidence of their presence remained for a long time. The great wagon road, cut out in part from the solid rock, was claimed by British Columbians as 'the eighth wonder of the world'; the town sites were finished, the important parts of the land had been surveyed, substantial buildings left behind, much mapping done by old-fashioned lithography as well as new-fangled photography and even an observatory set up. For good measure they left behind them as assay office, a mint and the first savings bank. On no other part of the Empire did the hand of the Royal Engineers rest more heavily. Many excellent photographs exist to prove it.

Palmer, at 24, had much valuable work behind him but it was only a beginning. With many comprehensive maps and reports over his signature filed away for all time in Parliamentary and Colonial Blue Books, and lectures given to, among others, the Royal Geographical Society, it was inevitable that his next posting should be to the Ordnance Survey. In 1867 Mr Disraeli's leap in the dark designed to give something like universal male franchise called into existence a new Parliamentary Boundaries Commission. Palmer, by then a Captain, was based on Tonbridge and responsible for the surveys of Kent, East Sussex and parts of Berkshire and

Buckinghamshire. On the strength of this he was named as Assistant Commissioner for defining the limits of the parliamentary boroughs of Kent and a part of the adjoining counties.

It was this unexciting task that, quite accidentally, led Palmer on to his next exploit. Among the parliamentary boundaries to be settled, the most important thereabouts were those of Maidstone, the Prime Minister's own constituency. Not far from the county town and hard by the beautiful little Leeds Castle lay the village of Ulcombe. It was an unremarkable place but it had a remarkable parson. Even in an age when every parish priest was expected to be, and usually was, a scholar and a gentleman the Rev. Pierce Butler stood out above most others. Apart from being a junior member of the once ducal house of Ormonde he and his brother had been intrepid travellers in the Holy Land and were fluent Arabic speakers. The duties of the Ordnance Survey required its officers to visit every Rector and Vicar in their bailiwicks with a view to finding out what was to be known of any places of antiquarian interest that might be worthy of appearing in their maps and Captain Palmer found the Butlers to be men of his own kind. In 1853, at their own expense, they had made the hazardous crossing of the Sinai Peninsula and were eager that a properly equipped expedition should be mounted to make a survey of the place which had hardly seen a European since Napoleon's team of explorers had visited it at the end of the previous century. More in hope than anticipation the Butlers and Palmer made such plans as could be made from the comfort of Ulcombe Rectory.

Most fortunately, the time and the men came together, for mid-Victorian England had suddenly discovered an interest in religious affairs. The Oxford Movement and its Puseyites were a recent memory and men had begun to look at religion as Charles Darwin had looked at science. All those Biblical placenames, long regarded as being about as real as Camelot and Lyonesse, had for centuries been swallowed up in an Ottoman Empire that did not encourage tourists. All of a sudden the Turk, displaying some degree of gratitude for having been rescued in the Crimean War, was showing himself slightly more amiable. The Prince and Princess of Wales had spent a couple of months in Palestine during the Spring of 1862. Thus encouraged, the Archbishop of York had convened a meeting of many eminent persons in order to form a Society 'for the investigation of the archaeology, topography, geology and manners and customs of the Holy Land'. Under the name of 'The Palestine Exploration Fund' it came into existence in 1865 with the novelist Walter Besant as its first secretary. The Fund caught the public fancy and preparations were made very quickly for its first foray. At the same moment as the Church was interesting itself, the State also took a hand. Dean Stanley of Westminster, on behalf of a Committee headed by the Bishop of London, formally requested the Secretary for War, Lord Grey, to arrange for a regular survey to made of Jerusalem. It seemed a natural task for the Engineers and, ostensibly, its object would be the improvement of water supply and sanitation for the benefit of the numerous pilgrims then expected. The War Office was well disposed, not for reasons of piety but because plans for a Suez Canal were taking shape and accurate maps of an area of such high strategic importance would be needed. The first man to be consulted was Palmer's uncle, Sir Henry James. When asked to price the survey he came up with the figure of £500. How he calculated this is unclear. The pay of a Sapper Captain in British Columbia had been £535 a year, more than that of his infantry grandson in the 1940s. In any case there was no vote that covered it. By undisclosed means the philanthropist Miss Angela Burdett Coutts, who had already met the bill for providing British Columbia with its Bishop, was persuaded to put up the money. Her vast fortune usually plugged such gaps.

The War Office lived up to its reputation. It would, if asked, furnish the services of an officer of the Royal Engineers, but somebody else must pay him. Sir Henry, knowing quite well that his fairly recently married nephew — who had had no business to marry at 24 — was in no position to work for charity, nominated Lieutenant Charles Wilson RE, lately Secretary to the Boundary Commission, who was willing to go on the basis that for two months in the year he would be treated as being on paid leave and for the remainder he would receive regimental pay only. The History of the Ordnance Survey, after enumerating Wilson's experience, adds cryptically that he might also have hoped for financial assistance from his own family. This is hard to understand, for the Wilsons were not rich. Nevertheless, he went, with a sergeant, two lance-corporals and a couple of sappers.

The party reached Jerusalem in October, 1864, ordered to be back again by February, 1865, with complete maps, town plan, photographs, geological specimens, fossils and much else. The task was an impossible one and it is greatly to Wilson's credit that he managed as much as he did, the more so when one learns from his report of the heat, the roughness of the terrain and the general filth of the area.

Palmer, meanwhile, was pressing his Uncle Henry to be allowed to make a further survey in company with his friend Pierce Butler and eventually he overbore that autocratic man. The Royal Geographical Society and the Royal Society agreed to help out with money, on the understanding that the expedition would 'elucidate the topography of the Exodus and make a general survey of the geology, botany and zoology of the region'. Sad to say, Pierce Butler did not live to see it. He died early in 1868. The work still went on and Palmer gathered together a party of highly competent men. Wilson, whom he had known in British Columbia, was one; another was Palmer's unrelated namesake, the remarkable Edward Henry Palmer, then aged 28.

Edward Palmer is generally described as 'Professor Palmer, the distinguished Arabist', but there was more to him than that. His father had owned a private school near Cambridge and had died young, leaving the boy to be brought up by a maiden aunt. He early contracted the habit of using his school holidays to live with the gypsies and his knowledge of their ways and language were fully equal to that of George Borrow. As a clerk in the City he sought out the company of the Italians who ground organs and, as in Conan Doyle's *The Six Napoleons,* made and sold plaster-cast images. From them he learnt fluent Italian. His friends were many and various, including Henry Irving, and he amused himself and others by demonstrations of strange mesmeric powers. In 1860, after a serious illness, he returned to Cambridge and became friends with Seyyid Abdullah, the teacher of Hindustani at the University, from whom he picked up another language. From Hindustani he went on to learn idiomatic Arabic and Persian; by the age of 22 he was writing Persian verses. His talents became so well known that he was admitted to the University where he catalogued the Persian, Arabic and Turkish MSS. Within a few years he was recognised as one of the leading experts in oriental languages although it was not until 1867 that he set foot outside England. His fame reached the knowledge of Walter Besant and he was invited to join the survey party. His particular charge was to collect the correct place names from local Bedouin in order to establish the definitive nomenclature of the Sinai Peninsula.

The party, thus completed and reinforced by four Sappers, arrived in Sinai on 12 November, 1868. Its orders were to produce a manuscript map of as large an area as possible on a scale of 2 inches to the mile, paying particular attention to the traditional Mountain of the Law and the famous monastery of Saint Catherine. It was hard work, for the country was as rugged as could be and the climate awful. Nevertheless, it was done. Though the survey was necessarily sketchy a lot of it was worth having. The run-down fortresses spanning the peninsula — El Arish, Nakhl and Aqaba — were all examined with a view to judging their military usefulness. Edward Palmer made himself responsible for Nakhl, the central one, by taking coffee there with the Egyptian police chief in charge of the place, followed by a pipe-smoking on the divan in the barely furnished great hall. He did not think much of Nakhl or its tenants: 'A wretched square fort in the midst of a glaring desert plain, the picture being backed up with some rather pretty limestone mountains. None of the soldiers were in uniform and they were as scoundrelly a set as one could well conceive.'

The Monastery of St Catherine, at the foot of Mount Sinai, was another matter. Monasteries had existed thereabouts since the beginning of the Christian era but had been raided so frequently by the Bedouin that life had become nearly impossible. In the course of her famous journey in 327, seeking the True Cross, the Empress Helena, mother of Constantine, visited the mountain, saw what was happening and had a tower of refuge built; this developed into a regularly occupied monastery, still thriving, whose monks were amiably disposed to the English. In 1914, when a Turkish invasion seemed imminent, they were armed by Kitchener with British rifles which they expressed themselves willing to use in defence of their hermitage. Fortunately it was never necessary. The view from the summit, once enjoyed by Moses, was a vast panorama stretching over Arabia Petraea in one direction and 200 miles into Egypt in another. There was one interesting resident whom the Palmers may or may not have met. In 1845 another of the race of free-range Scotsmen, a Major Macdonald, had settled with his wife at the foot of Mount Maghara in a dauntless quest for commercial exploitation of the turquoise deposits that exist thereabouts. It was a rare example of time's whirligig. On the edge of the cradle of the human race, where men had lived in cities long before the first Macdonalds had left their caves, the Scotsman improved his leisure time by teaching their descendants the lost art of building in stone instead of mud. The rubbings he made of early dynastic inscriptions are still in the British Museum. He died there a year after the expedition left.

Some time was to elapse before the strategic importance of the place was plain to everybody, but it required only a map to show it. Lord Cromer needed no instruction. When the Turks, on behalf of Germany, proposed to run a railway through the Peninsula he minuted to Sir Edward Grey that 'The proposed line would have the effect of rendering the Gulf of Akaba more available for torpedo-boats which would lie on the flank of the route to India and within easy striking distance of that route.' This was the kernel of the business and it had become true as soon as British troopships had begun using the Canal. Every morsel of information was needed by the Foreign Office, the Admiralty and the War Office. Palmer's expedition may have been held out as being of cultural interest and no doubt it was. All the same, it was not information about monasteries and turquoise mines that Whitehall was seeking.

When the party returned home in the following May the Treasury was sufficiently interested to put up £500 towards the cost of having the results reduced into writing. Three fat volumes were produced in which everybody had a hand. Captain Palmer's contribution was the maps, plans and sections. The third volume was something new, good reproductions of half the 300 photographs they had taken. As a separate item there was a box containing thirty-six stereoscopic views complete with stereoscope.

Several years were to pass before another Sapper finished off the job of a complete survey. Between November, 1883, and April, 1884, Major H. H. Kitchener, accompanied by the geologist Professor Hull and once more at the request and cost of the Fund, went off on their camels and triangulated some 3,000 square miles from Aqaba to the Dead Sea. The scorching glare from the sun nearly cost Kitchener his eyesight and left him with the famous squint. In a proper and soldier-like way he had refused to wear his dark glasses when his companions had none.

1869 was a spectacular year for the Near East. Charles Wilson and the other archaeologically-minded Sapper, Charles Warren, still busy in Jerusalem, entertained distinguished visitors; the Emperor of Austria and the Crown Prince of Prussia visited the Holy City in November. Though it was only three years since Sadowa they may have decided that the French were taking over too much and a common Teutonic front was desirable. There could be no question about which nation was top dog in the Levant during that year and spectacular evidence was at hand when in the course of the same month the Empress of the French attended by her beauty chorus sailed triumphantly through the Canal built by her cousin M. de Lesseps almost to the accompaniment of *Ritorna Vincitor* and the other music composed for the occasion by Signor Verdi. All the same, there was a strong Sapper presence to balance things out. The model campaign by General Sir Robert Napier at the other end of the Red Sea, during which his column had marched nearly 400 miles through daunting country and rescued the hostages held by King Theodore of Abyssinia with hardly a life lost, was still a very recent memory. In addition to the military there were several private gentlemen who had been drawn to the area by reason of the modishness caused by the Canal opening.

John Macgregor — 'Rob Roy' Macgregor — had once more brought his canoe along after an absence of twenty years and was adding the Nile, the Jordan and several other Near Eastern rivers to his game-book. Macgregor was a considerable man by any standard. As a serious scholar he had a Master's degree from Oxford. As a philanthropist he had, in some fashion, organized the London shoeblacks and was in the habit of distributing Anglican tracts to all manner of bewildered recipients. One paragraph from one of his books, long out of print, deserves preservation: 'Music floats over the air of Egypt as "backshish" in Turkey proper and "dollar" in the land of the West. Crossing the Missouri in Kansas I thought there at least I was out of the range of Scotchmen and of dollars: but in the ferry boat the only other passenger was a Macdonald and from the opposite shore the first word, shouted at an auction, was "dollar".' His most spectacular achievement was to gain the coveted 'Royal' prefix for his Canoe Club and to enlist as its Commodore the unlikeliest canoeist of them all, Albert Edward Prince of Wales. His book, (one of several, describing voyages all over the place), *The Rob Roy On The Jordan* is still a splendid read. All other things apart, it is interesting to learn how, in 1869, the inflatable mattress, the liquid-filled compass and Liebig's extract of meat were in use and French officers wore 'a hat very like a parasol, the top being distant from the head of the wearer several inches all round and connected by three wires to a leather-bound iron ring which goes on the temples.' Macgregor was a considerable figure in the Levant and widely respected. He devoted much time to ascertaining the exact crossing-place of the Children of Israel and placed it at the mouth of the Sweetwater Canal; local tradition agreed with him, for the name of Jews Island still persisted. The identification by the Palmers of the Mountain of the Law was confirmed by Dr Beke in 1874.

As Professor Palmer — the title was not his until 1871 but he is always known by it — now leaves the story it may be worth a moment's digression to tell what happened to him. He had been unsettled by his travels and took against academic life. He became a journalist, travelled much in the Levant, became friends with Sir Richard Burton and on one occasion walked alone the 600 miles from Sinai to Jerusalem. His influence over the Bedouin was equalled only by that of Kitchener and Lawrence but in the end he pressed his luck too hard. At the time of Arabi's rebellion against the Khedive, which was to end with Sir Garnet Wolseley's Egyptian expedition, the Admiralty badly needed help in preparing the ground for whatever might have to be done. Mr Gladstone was persuaded to send Captain William Gill, RE, a famous Intelligence Officer who had worked in Central Asia, to drum up support for the anti-Arabi faction, if one existed, in Sinai and, incidentally, to buy camels against the day they might be needed. Professor Palmer, who knew everybody among the sheikhs, accompanied him along with £3,000 in gold. The Royal Navy was represented by Lieutenant Charrington of the brewing family. At a spot near Nakhl they were offered hospitality by Bedouin well known to Palmer who led them to a cliff top where they were shot in the back, tossed over the edge and their bodies mutilated. A roar of rage went up in England. Colonel Charles Warren, RE, was given the task of rounding up the murderers and hanging them. He had better success with his investigations than was to come his way a few years later when, as Commissioner of the Metropolitan Police, he was put to hunting Jack the Ripper. The crime was certainly carried out on the orders of Arabi who, presumably, inherited the money. By popular demand the remains were brought home and buried in St. Paul's. In his short life Professor Palmer had written over a dozen books of great authority on most aspects of the Near East including a history of Jerusalem written jointly with Walter Besant. It was he who finally proved the Dome of the Rock to have been built in 691 by the Caliph Abd-el-Melik and not, as was generally thought, by the Emperor Constantine.

The Sinai survey ended Captain Palmer's work in the Near East. In 1873, by then a Major, he was suggested by the Astronomer Royal to the Admiralty as being the right man to go to New Zealand in order to observe the transit of Venus, something that had been suggested by Halley as long ago as 1716, but the last word had yet to be said. Palmer, who had a taste for astronomy, was sent on a course to the Royal Observatory under Sir George Airy, who, though now 72, was still one of the first scientists of the day. One of his tasks since being appointed in 1835 had been conducting the preliminary observations necessary for fixing the boundaries between Canada and the United States. Thus there was some common ground between them. Airy formed a high opinion of the Sapper officer, sufficient to entrust him with charge of the party. With a naval lieutenant and a Sapper subaltern, along with several NCOs who were trained photographers, Palmer embarked for New Zealand in June, 1874. The work was not sufficiently animating to call for detailed description but the Astronomer Royal gave it high praise in his annual report. The Governor of New Zealand, Lord Normanby, was not going to let slip the chance of making a highly-trained Sapper earn his keep in the Colony. For several months Palmer was kept up to the collar by investigating the chaotic state of such provincial surveys as had been made and devising a way in which they could be produced and maintained on a proper scientific basis. His recommendations were gratefully received and incorporated once more into a Blue Book. Then, beginning in 1876, followed a tour in the West Indies as Resident Engineer in Barbados and ADC to Mr Pope-Hennessy, the Governor of the Windward Islands. It was not a good time to arrive. The Governor had only just proclaimed a confederation of the islands which was bitterly opposed by the planters. On the principle that if the planters were against it then confederation must be a good thing, the black population noisily approved it. When no obvious advantages followed at once they rioted and destroyed much property, then squared up to the police who shot a number of them. The planters panicked. Order was soon restored but relations between the groups of inhabitants took a long time to settle down. Major Palmer had only a year of it. By April, 1878, he was back in Hong Kong, this time to draw up plans for the Observatory. His report went to the Royal Society whose Committee at Kew endorsed every word of it. The usual economies were made when the observatory came to be built but it was still considered highly successful and a model of what such things should be in future.

His Astronomical, Magnetical, Meteorological and Tidal work done, Palmer decided to take a look at Japan before going home. This led to a meeting with one of the most remarkable men of the century and some of the strangest duties ever laid upon a regular officer of the Royal Engineers.

Harry Parkes was the son of a Walsall ironmaster and had had the misfortune to lose both parents early in his life. His uncle, a retired naval officer, was saddled with bringing up both Harry and his two sisters. He made a noble effort to do his family duty but cannot have found it easy. In 1841, at the age of 13, Harry was packed off to China where his sisters were already settled in the home of a married cousin whose husband was secretary to the British Chief Superintendent of Trade at Macao. At 14 he found himself caught up in the First Opium War in the service of Sir Henry Pottinger during his punitive expedition up the Yangtse. Parkes, who had a talent for languages and was a young man of great charm, made himself useful as a forager and had a small hand in the attack on Chinkiang. When the treaty was signed at Nanking on 29 August, 1842, he was among the grandees present and a few months later he formally entered the Consular service at 15. For the next twenty years Harry Parkes was continually active as his country's spokesman during the long period of wars and near-wars, experiencing all the cruelty and bad faith that governed the doings of the Celestial Empire and its servants. He displayed great personal bravery on many occasions, became an intimate friend of Gordon and Napier and was saved from being murdered in a Chinese prison only by the French General Montauban's victory at Palikao. It was Harry Parkes who was responsible for opening up the Treaty Ports following upon the Treaty of Tientsin and in 1862 he was made KCB at the unheard of age of 34. In 1865 he was upgraded from Consulate to Diplomatic service and appointed Minister to Japan.

By the time Parkes and Palmer met, Sir Harry's eighteen years in Japan were nearly over. Even more than in China he had been the voice of Britain after the anarchy and civil war of the late 1860s and had been, as his biographer says, 'identified with every forward movement towards unification and assimilation to western civilisation. He had helped in the introduction of the first railways, had settled the currency, opened the port of Kobe to foreigners and had more than once fought off murderous attacks by crusted Tories with two-handed swords. Such was the esteem in which the Emperor held him that he was, unprecedentedly, offered the Grand Cordon of the Rising Sun. Japan was well regarded in the late Victorian age and the British Government was mildly gratified at being invited to help in bringing the country forward by a few centuries. It was at Parkes' suggestion that the Japanese authorities asked Palmer to undertake a task that might cause even the most experienced sapper to hesitate. Could Colonel Palmer, as he now was, please build them a waterworks at Yokohama? The idea was tempting and a question of face was involved. Palmer, whatever his private misgivings may have been, agreed to take it on.

Lord Salisbury, who had succeeded Mr Gladstone in the same year, was of like mind. It can only have been coincidence but 1885 was the year that also saw the first production of Mr Gilbert's *The Mikado* with music by Dr. Sullivan. Not everybody who saw it realized the opera to be a little joke at the expensive of the English and nothing at all to do with Japan, but it did not matter. Certainly not to Lord Salisbury; one of the few remarks about music which are attributed to him is still famous: 'There's a man called Brahms. He's the worst of the lot.' More to the point was the Imperial Japanese Navy which was of much interest to Britain as both pupil and customer. The Royal Navy was already thoroughly at home in Japan, with pink-faced midshipmen infesting Nikko in search of more or less innocent fun. Add to that the fact that Mr Disraeli's dictum 'Sanitas sanitatum, omnia sanitas' still carried a message and it was obvious why the work had to be done and done, for preference, by an Englishman.

When Palmer arrived home he was appointed Commanding Engineer at Manchester. This was no accident, for Manchester was the one place in England where much was going on in the water supply business. A few decades earlier the town had been notorious as one of the worst slums created by the Industrial Revolution, but all that was now changing. Plans had been made for the lake of Thirlmere to be laid under contribution and the best brains in the business were at work on bringing its clean supply to a growing city. Palmer learned all there was to be learned and, thus taught, he returned to Japan almost at once. It can only be conjecture but in all probability the waterworks of Yokohama were designed on the banks of the Irk.

It was a time when no expatriate Englishman earning his living in the island Empire need have felt himself condemned to outer darkness. The Tokyo Club had been founded in 1884 and modelled itself on Pall Mall. It was, of course, strictly for men only, with 'supporting members' from the Imperial family, 'special members' drawn from Ambassadors and diplomats; the hard core, described as 'gentlemen both Japanese and foreign' were mostly in trade, however much they might try to disguise it. There were exceptions, for Japan was still much under foreign tutelage. One such, whom it is fair to suppose was known by Palmer, was Captain John Ingles RN; his description was 'British adviser to the Navy Ministry'. In fact he was the brains of the Naval War College and bore some responsibility for the creation of an Imperial Navy with history running from Tsushima to Tokyo Bay forty years later. The Royal Navy occupied a place in public veneration hard now to believe. When Mr Belasco came to write his play about 'Madame Butterfly' he had no need to hesitate about making his ignoble hero Benjamin Franklin Pinkerton an American officer. He would never have dared to put him in the Queen's senior service.

Although it had been the navy of the United States which had opened the gates of Japan in the 1850s there was still less of an American presence than might have been expected. When Rudyard

Kipling visited the country in 1889 he reckoned to have seen three Englishmen for every American, but his stay was short and his travels unextensive. There were Consuls from every nation in Europe, as well as from the USA, exercising jurisdiction over their own nationals in the Treaty Ports. The French abounded, as they seemed to do everywhere. The Japanese Army had begun as an imitation of the French but after 1870 had turned over to German instructors and suppliers, though many entrepreneurs remained. The British had supplied engineers since about the same time, building and running the railways between Yokohama and Tokyo, with lines to Kobe, Osaka and Kyoto joining in later. Mr Brunton had set up the system of lighthouses, and other civilians were engaged with electric telegraphs and teaching of science to young Japanese. American expertise did, however, show itself in affairs that it did best. There were, by the mid-80s, some excellent hotels. The Grand at Yokohama was already quite famous; postcards of the day show it as being not far short of London's second-best. Palmer would not have lacked for company of his own kind. This is not mere surmise. His obituary in the *Japan Weekly Mail* for 18 February, 1893, tells of 'an exceptionally handsome wreath from the members of the Tokyo Club, where the presence of the genial and gifted officer had been a frequent attraction during many years of the Club's existence'. It ends: 'In everyday life he showed a keen appreciation of humour, and his powers of anecdote made him a delightful companion whose memory will long be cherished by a wide circle of friends and admirers.' For a man planning a new civilian career there are advantages in being clubbable and Henry Palmer had more and better anecdotes on call than did most men.

It was in 1887, the year of the Queen's Jubilee, that Henry Palmer decided to quit her service and strike out for himself. His part in the Yokohama project was finished, save for giving advice, and the work was well under way. He genuinely liked the country and its people and they got on well together. There was no reason why he should not turn his natural talents and professional training to advantage and, if he could, make for his family and himself a modest fortune. In a country where official rank of some sort was essential for both social acceptance and professional advancement, Palmer was already secure; the Emperor had appointed him 'Foreign

Adviser to the Department of Home Affairs'; his friend and fellow clubman the American Henry Willard Denison doubled the roles of US Consul and 'Personal Adviser to the Foreign Minister', Prince Inoue Kaoru. It was not a matter of some unknown civilian expert putting up a brass plate and waiting for customers. The Emperor, with a proper appreciation of qualities uncommon either within or without his Empire, marked Palmer's work at Yokohama with the Grant of the Order of the Rising Sun (Third Class) and commissions flowed in. Because he was known for the business of waterworks Palmer was invited to design one for Kobe; before that was finished he was set to drawing up a scheme for a large irrigation-syphon at Misakamura and superintending the building of it. He planned the construction of a water supply to Tokyo itself, which was not completed until after his death. There were also engagements higher than those of a glorified Borough Engineer. The Japanese Navy, and Captain Ingles, wanted Yokohama Harbour, the country's main port of entry, enlarged and improved. Harbours are not usually reckoned sapper work but officers of the Corps can turn their hands to anything. During the summer of 1888 Palmer drew up, against heavy competition, such a scheme, along with his plans for a Repair Basin and a Graving Dock. They met with Imperial approval and Palmer was placed in charge of their execution. It was a long business and he did not live to see the end of it. On 10 February, 1893, Henry Spencer Palmer, 55 years old and at the top of his particular ladder, died suddenly. His death was much felt in the capital, for Palmer had long since set himself the task of trying to explain Japan to England; his letters to *The Times* had been many and eloquent. It was, perhaps, merciful that he did not live to see the other face of Japan.

The Emperor gave him a fine funeral. Archdeacon Shaw conducted the service, a battalion of Japanese infantry led the cortège and all the diplomats, along with everybody else who was anybody, followed in their carriages with a great multitude walking behind. Major-General Palmer, though not renowned in war, lies in Tokyo not far from other British soldiers of a later day.

From the Bella Coola by way of Sinai, Hong Kong, New Zealand and Japan is a notable journey. In case your Latin has grown rusty, 'paene' means 'almost' or 'nearly', 'Ubique' you will not need translated.

VII

Egypt And The Sudan:
Sir Colin Scott-Moncrieff

ONCE UPON A TIME, centuries or millennia before
Ozymandias, unremembered Kings of Egypt built canals long
forgotten. They had to, for even in the dawn of the world the
people of the Delta would have starved without them. One
commodity the ancient world had almost to excess; people abounded
and people needed to be fed and watered. As they had nothing else
to give to the community they could give their labour in exchange
for their keep. This they did, from remotest times until quite
recently. In gangs of thousands they dug irrigation canals, from
Memphis to the site of Cairo, from the Nile to Fayum and the
Red Sea. Thousands of years passed between the carrying out of
these various operations; thousands more would elapse before the
first of what might be called the modern works were put in hand,
by those unlucky enough to be swept up for the corvée.

Napoleon Bonaparte had come and gone, his plans for mastery
of Europe with the help of the East wrecked by Nelson and the
Royal Navy. In 1805, Trafalgar year, the Viceroy of Egypt under
the Sultan in Constantinople addressed his mind to the problem
of how to domesticate the Nile and compel it to water his crops
all year round.

Egypt and its neighbour which we call the Sudan had the
advantage of never being touched by any of the Ice Ages. This
ensured what Kinglake called 'a birthless past and a future that has
no end'. Nobody can say with any certainty when these ancient
lands first settled down into fortified cities and organized national
families. Unlike the vanished inhabitants of ancient India, long
forgotten races have left their buildings and memorials plain to

be seen by those who came after. They have also left it to posterity to think out for itself why peoples capable of carrying out these mighty works should have degenerated into what is now seen. Kinglake put at any rate some of the explanation down to plague, brought about by lack of attention to the humbler forms of civil engineering such as sewerage.

One thing is certain and always has been since homo became more or less sapiens. The Nile is everything. Generation after generation, Ruskin's swallows have looked down on the strip of green that alone stands out in the umber and gamboge of the African landscape below them. It is, indeed, no ordinary river; in length it exceeds the distance from Liverpool to New York or from New York to San Francisco. And it contains just about every good and bad quality that a deity could put together.

In the first place it has habits as regular as the tides of the sea and appears always to have observed them. Only in the later days of Queen Victoria did anybody know the reason. Until the inquisitive English arrived nobody bothered much about it. The business was supernatural and the river was a God in its own right. Sceptical Europeans were tolerably sure that in some Rider Haggard country the Nile rose in much the same fashion as other rivers but it took a long time to find out the truth of it. The White Nile, after leaving Lake Albert, meanders for about 140 miles more or less on the level and then the descent begins. During the next 100 the great body of water drops down some 750 feet before flattening itself out again for the next 1150 where it shares it bed with an obstructive vegetable growth known as the sudd. So far, indeed as far as Khartoum, the river had done nothing more useful than create some mighty swamps and mightier insect life. Once there, the Blue Nile comes in from the right and produces regularly every August and September a volume of water rushing down at the rate of half a million gallons a second. That done, the Blue Nile has shot its bolt and for the following six months it is the White Nile that nurtures Egypt. Nevertheless it is the Blue Nile which has brought from the mountains of Ethiopia the other commodity upon which Egypt and the Egyptians depend utterly for their bare existence. Glorious red mud, the soldier's curse and the fellah's delight, comes tumbling in suspension down the river, 85,000 tons of it in a good year. As it has to travel something like 2,000 miles before the last traces of it tint the Mediterranean it is hardly wonderful that the land it fertilizes cannot manage to detain much more than a third of it.

Once Khartoum is left behind the unified river begins its gigantic water-slide, along a reach of 60 miles past the ruins of Meroe and down to the first (officially the Sixth) of the cataracts. Once having pushed its way through and having been reinforced by its last tributary the Atbara — Bahr el Aswad, the Black River — the water takes on the sand and overcomes it. Traces, barely visible now, in the western Sahara show where other long-vanished rivers tried to do the same but were swallowed up by the stronger element. Only the Nile has the power to drive irresistibly through the barren desert, round the Great Bend with its three cataracts. Then across the Bayuda desert to Wadi Halfa, where the still visible ruins of ancient Egypt really begin, it continues the downhill rush to the sea, cascading vigorously down the largest cataract of all, the speed of its passage through the narrow gap between the granite and porphyry rocks being made with what one writer has called 'unwanted impetuosity'. The mass of water then slows down, apparently exhausted by this display of energy. The gradient from then onwards becomes no more than a couple of inches to the mile and the anabasis continues for the rest of the way at no more than a moderate walking pace. The last 120 miles from Cairo to the sea flank the Delta where grows almost everything that Egypt produces. Sir Robert Wilson (of whom more later) tells of what he saw in the year 1801. 'The waters of the Nile begin to increase annually on the 16th June, old style, which answers to our 27th. Opposite to Old Cairo is the key of the water, or Nilometer, a house so called, built upon pillars in the middle of the river. In this house is a bason, with a column in the centre, on which are cut figures of measurement, and as these marks are covered by the rising of the waters, the criers daily proclaim the height throughout the streets of the city. The river rises gradually till it increases to fifteen or sixteen spans, as they say, to which height it usually attains on the sixteenth of July, old style. On that day the Pacha, attended by all the Beys, goes in procession by land to a Kiosk, or summer house, built on the banks of the river; and in the mouths of the canals, multitudes of people assemble in barges and boats. On a signal given by the Pacha, the workmen directly open the mouth of the canal,* and as the water then rushes into it, the Pacha throw handfuls of silver coins into the stream and the Arabs diving after the money are allowed to take away as much as they can get. In the same moment the people in thousands of boats rush into the canal, and with the sound of vocal and many species of instrumental music, join to express their joy on the occasion.' Entirely understandable this, for the ceremony was every bit as momentous as any Dionysiac Rite of Spring. The largesse seems to have been thrown at all High Niles, though the tide-mark on the Nilometer indicated whether Egypt during the coming season would live or die. If it showed less than 20 feet it meant famine. 30 feet or more spelt ruin by flood. The most usual measurement of 23 to 25 feet assured all hands of full bellies for one more year. Other plagues of Egypt were in the nature of bonuses.

For generations the riverside had been embanked, with other embankments running off at right angles to higher ground, dividing the country into basins of sizes varying between 3,000 and 60,000 acres in area. Short canals through the river banks allowed water and mud to come in and flood the place; when October came and the water ebbed away, ploughing and sowing could take place with reaping and mowing following in April. With that done the basins baked themselves in sunshine until the river rose again. All this was well enough if only grain and vegetables were needed. It would not serve for cotton, a plant that demands water during the periods when the river gives none. Nobody seemed greatly exercised about this until there appeared on the scene one of the most interesting men of the 19th century.

When Napoleon Bonaparte dreamed up the idea of conquering the world by using the manpower of the East he was far from enjoying an hallucination. In the words of the hymn, the lands of the East might awake and their sons should be free. The first part of the stanza nearly came true, to the discomfiture of many, and the cause of it may well have been the legacy of Bonaparte. His successor, Mehemet Ali, began his career keeping a small shop at Cavalla in Roumelia. Finding this unfulfilling, he became some sort of irregular soldier, learned the elements of the trade in

* 'A canal traverses the city from south to north and divides it into two parts'

suppressing the pirates of Crete and graduated to the British service as commander of an Albanian free corps under Sir Ralph Abercromby in Egypt. When a vacuum was left there after both French and British had gone, Mehemet filled it. The Sultan, having little choice in the matter, created him Viceroy. How he bit the hand that fed him by coming close to taking Constantinople from his master is a splendid story but no part of this one. It is, however, relevant to mention his disposal of the party in opposition to him. The Mamelukes, roughly the local Samurai, were formidable but not over-bright. When the Viceroy invited them all to a great tamasha in the Citadel, they went. As soon as they were immured in the quadrangle Mehemet's Albanians, who were famous marksmen, quickly despatched the lot, shooting from above with nothing to spoil their aim. That done, Mehemet could attend to parish business.

His energy was much admired. Even that stout Churchman 'Rob Roy' Macgregor found himself able to praise him. 'That wonderful man,' he calls him, adding helpfully that 'his amazing energies come not from the lotus-eaters of the Nile. He was no true Ottoman Turk, but rather a Seljakian Koniarat of Cavalla, whatever all that means'. Another admirer was that quintessential mid-Victorian sea-officer Commodore Charles Napier.* Napier felt the removal of the opposition a little raw: 'It is true that they were troublesome gentlemen and had they lived would in all probability have destroyed the Pacha; but nothing can excuse the treacherous manner in which he accomplished his object.' All the same, no Mameluke would have taken on the Nile as Mehemet was to do. Many years later Napier reported on him again: 'Egypt is making rapid strides to improvement and is now beginning to feel the advantages of Mehemet Ali's system,' he wrote after a visit in 1841, adding, rather unkindly, that 'He is, it is true, an Oriental, and has many mistaken notions; but he must be treated with kindness and consideration.'

Some of Mehemet's notions, were, however, entirely sensible.

* A. W. Kinglake, in *Eothen,* quotes Lady Hester Stanhope as saying that 'amongst the English of all ranks and all classes there is no man so attractive to the Orientals, no man who can negotiate with them half so effectively, as a good, honest, open-hearted and positive naval officer of the old school.' She might have had Charlie Napier in mind.

He grasped the idea that something had to be done about regulating the progress of the waters of the Nile between Cairo and the sea and that the place where that something had to be done was the point where the Rosetta and Damietta branches part company about 14 miles below Cairo. A barrage of some kind should be able to control the water even if it would conserve none. The same idea had occurred to General Bonaparte in 1798 but Fate and the Royal Navy had got in first. More than once since Abercromby's day Mehemet had had what Ned McGowan would have called 'a difficulty' with the British. Accordingly he sought his engineering advisers among the French. Linant Bey, otherwise M. Linant de Bellefonds, was the first of them and he arrived just in time. Mehemet was on the point of damming the Rosetta — the western — branch so effectively that it would have cut off the water supply to Alexandria. Linant suggested that a better plan would be to erect a barrage across both branches so that the flow of water could be regulated in summer but leave the river to find its own level during flood time. Mehemet was captivated. Let the work be started at once. If stone were needed the Bey had his leave to dismantle the Pyramid of Giza for the purpose. The work began without this necessity and vast numbers of fellahin did their corvée on barrage-building. Then in 1835 the plague came (it was still raging years later when Kinglake arrived), great number of them died and everything stopped. Mehemet became bored. He remained so for the next seven years; lean years for the fellah, but fat ones for every sort of corrupt official.

It is only fair to Mehemet to remark that he had on his mind matters even more pressing than the barrages. Though he had been denied the prize of Constantinople by a rare piece of European concertry, he had been given Syria as a consolation prize. By 1839 his overlord Mahmoud II felt strong enough to try and wrest it back. The concert of Europe struck up again, Mehemet was defeated outside Beirut and Alexandria was being blockaded. With such unfair odds against him, Mehemet became the diplomat and struck an excellent bargain. His non-existent claims on Syria were waived in exchange for the hereditary Pashalik of Egypt. That settled, Mehemet turned once more to improving his dominions and began by hiring another French engineer. M. Mougel — henceforth Mougel Bey — designed a new barrage, one for either branch, each with iron gates able to hold up a depth of about 20 feet of water. Though his Council of Bridges & Roads spurned the idea, the Pasha, in one of his bursts of energy, ordered Mougel to proceed. He could be persuasive when he wished to be. An Egyptian engineer, asked how long it would take to cut a certain canal, demanded a year. 200 strokes from the bastinado, with a promise of another 300 if there was any more nonsense, made sure that the job was completed in four months. Mougel did not fear for his feet. Abd-el-Kader and various others could have told Mehemet that France was not in a mood to be humbugged by wily orientals. He did, however, fear for his well-paid job; when the Pasha announced that 1,000 cubic metres of concrete were to be laid every day the Bey jumped to it. He was able to report, truthfully, that the order had been carried out. It was not for him to embroider truth by adding that at one end it had been put into the shallowest of foundation trenches and at the other much of it had instantly been washed away. Nor that a flexible mix of concrete and quicksand was doing duty as a floor under some of the openings. Both Beys, Linant and Mougel, clung to their jobs after Mehemet Ali died in 1848, but not for long. Their Egyptian successors continued to build the two bridges, complete with roads, pathways and a pair of tastefully castellated turrets; all sat perilously on top of some outstandingly rotten foundations. Mougel came back to Egypt during the Crimean War and enjoyed a kind of revenge. Said Pasha, the then incumbent, was no Mehemet Ali but he was fascinated by matters military. By persuading him that the barrage could be made into a superior Lines of Chataldja the Bey was able to do something of a salvage operation. It had to be prettified by a kind of Vauban-and-water star fortress with 18th century trimmings. The Khedive Said highly approved.

The fact remained that the Nile Barrage, for all its rococo additions, was a whited sepulchre, full of dead men's bones and rottenness. Rob Roy Macgregor sailed his canoe under the Damietta bridge, followed by his luggage boat, in 1869 and during the two hours it took for the Governor and his officials to decide on the amount of dues payable he made some sketches. 'It acts as a long gate or weir across each of the two forks of the river, at the point of the Delta. The portion across the Damietta branch is about 600 yards long, and that over the Rosetta branch 500 yards. The weir consists of arches, each of 16 feet span. Of these there are 72 upon the Damietta branch. On the branch to Rosetta there are 62. Mehemet Ali died before any progress was made with this scheme, and his successor resolved to continue only the barrage proper without the canal, which formed its most important feature. At present it appears that the work has been entirely useless, and it is considered that, if any attempt were made to dam back the Nile by closing in the structure at high flood, the river would sweep away the whole mass together.' Macgregor was not quite right about the canals. The idea had been that, when the iron gates closing the arches were down, the held-up water would be diverted into three canals just upstream from the bridges. Some had been built but not anything like the entire system that had been planned. The central one had been restricted to a width of 50 feet by the Khedive's military adviser, for fear that anything bigger might encourage hostile warships. This ensured its inadequacy for irrigating the province it was designed to serve. The western canal had been excavated but was promptly abandoned to the desert which was not slow to reclaim its property. Best of all was the eastern section. When the first five miles had been completed the canal arrived at the edge of the estate of 'an influential Turkish lady'. Turkish ladies wanted no more of canals than did English noblemen of railways. In the face of a flat refusal the diggers could go no further. Turkish ladies of the day did not greatly interest themselves in the world outside. Macgregor came across an instance of it. 'Once, upon a steamboat, I observed a Turkish lady studying an atlas. The map represented Turkey not only as the centre of the earth but as occupying nearly all the circumference while England and America were two red dots on the farthest verge. I was generally spoken of as a native of Belad Ingleez — "the town of England".'

All this probably made little difference since the entire construction was crumbling. By 1871 the self-inflicted wounds were so nearly fatal that the Rosetta works had to be corsetted inside a great coffer-dam.

Thus things went on for the next dozen years or so, improvident and self-indulgent Khedives cheerfully bankrupting their country with either a touching faith in Kismet or something close to idiocy. Worst of the lot was Khedive Ismail. He did, at least, make some atonement by calling in British civil engineers — the Prussian war kept the favoured French out of the running — but when they announced that repairs would cost money he baulked. Money was designed for the procurement of assorted delights for rulers, not for ignorant peasantry. By 1876 matters had become desperate enough for them to be taken out of Ismail's hands. There was only one repository of the skills needed to discipline the world's great rivers and that was in India. The Sappers, Addiscombe men for the most part, were called in. It was not their first visit to Egypt. There had been several of them about the place when young Charles Pasley had enjoyed his holiday journey. Sir Robert Wilson, himself something of an adventurer, wrote a book in 1803 describing his experiences in Sir Ralph Abercromby's expedition which contains much more than pure military history. He wrote of 'Fourier, a gentleman of most considerable information, who made the discovery of the declination of the zodiac in the temples of Upper Egypt, and who proposed, in order to avoid distracting the world with any new theories, to publish his observations on that subject only in Latin, for the discussion only of the superior order of society.' Nor was M. Fourier intending to stop there. He was minded to produce a work of great authority to which all or most of Bonaparte's departed savants would contribute. 'Nouet gives the astronomical part; Ridouti* the natural history, and nothing can exceed the beauty of his drawings and other men of science the various other branches.' England would not lag behind. 'The public will also hereafter probably be gratified by some accounts on a smaller scale from Mr Hamilton, secretary to Lord Elgin, Lieut Hayes of the Engineers and Capt Legge of the Artillery who, since the conquest of Egypt, have penetrated farther than the French, proceeding near 100 miles beyond the Cataracts.'

The pause in the war caused by the Treaty of Amiens did much good for the French in the Levant. The British government, for entirely creditable reasons, was in no great hurry to evacuate Egypt. This worried Wilson. 'The Beys have been completely victorious over the Ottoman forces, having defeated them in five successive actions . . . While such is the state of things in Egypt the French influence in Constantinople is visibly gaining ground.'

* Pierre-Joseph Redouté (1759-1840), the most famous flower painter of them all.

France became demonstrably topdog throughout the whole area for a long time. Macgregor wrote bitterly about it from Beirut. 'While the English after the massacre of 1860 did the real work of helping the poor and the widow and the fatherless, the French blew their bugles and marched their Zouaves through the land.'

The first Sapper officer to be employed in Egypt during modern times was Major-General F. H. Rundall who was invited to advise on the problem in 1876. By that time the cause had altered and the French Republic had no mind for further oriental adventures just yet. Rundall's arrival more or less coincided with Mr Disraeli's purchase of the Suez Canal Company's shares, a transaction that established Britain's position firmly on the road to India.

The Nile continued to furnish Egypt with its annual bounty, but it needed help. None came for the present. Instead, upstream in the Sudan, the son of a Dongola boatbuilder announced himself to be the Prophet of God and sentenced his people to nearly twenty years of misery and war. This did nothing for the irrigation plans, though it did introduce to the country some of the great men of the Royal Engineers, quite apart from the fact that one of them was to bring down the Dervish Empire and convert the hellhole that had been Khartoum into a city with schools and hospitals. Practically all the grandees of the Corps were engaged in Egyptian affairs one way or another throughout the '80s and '90s of the last century. Their particular province was Suakin, that strange Red Sea port long since deserted by all but the cats. Sir Gerald Graham VC took the place over in February, 1884, a year before Gordon died; Herbert Chermside and Herbert Horatio Kitchener were among its more distinguished Governors, constantly at grips with Osman Digna's Fuzzie Wuzzies. For years to come it was the fighting side of the Royal Engineers that was in demand; civil engineering had to wait its turn.

British power came to Egypt in 1878 when, jointly with France, the Government took over the finances of a bankrupt country under the name of Dual Control. When Arabi's revolt came it was taken for granted that France would share in whatever naval or military action might be necessary. The French, however, had tired of using their army as a debt-collecting agency. Painful memories of what had happened when it tried to extract M. Jecker's money from Mexico and that of M. Dupont from Tonkin still lingered. Admiral Seymour bombarded Alexandria. Sir Garnet Wolseley slipped a Division through the Canal and routed the Egyptians at Tel-el-Kebir. Queen Victoria, however reluctantly, found herself governing another foreign country. Somebody had to take the responsibility and also to carry war to the Dervishes. There was no other candidate. There came also another responsibility. That of re-building the works on the Nile.

While other Sappers were commanding the forces that broke the Dervish attempt to invade Egypt and eventually took the war to their heartland, some of the Corps' officers were taken into government service in the customary quasi-civilian fashion. It was not before time. General Rundall had been one of Sir Arthur Cotton's 'most excellent set of officers' during the damming of the Godavari and he was a Cotton man through and through. A few years later he was invited to advise upon the possibility of building a Palestine Canal from a point on the Mediterranean coast to the Jordan Valley and then, by way of the Dead Sea and some enormous cuttings, to the Gulf of Aqaba. The idea had not got very far when it had to be abandoned since, in Colonel Sandes' words, 'the time was not ripe'. Nor was it ripe for tackling the Barrage seriously.

After Rundall came not another of Cotton's disciples but a man who had learned his trade in the rival establishment of Proby Cautley. Colin Campbell Scott-Moncrieff is one of the RE immortals, not so much for the outstanding and purely professional qualities of Cotton as for — once more to quote Colonel Sandes — 'courage, energy, sound judgment, common sense, unusual powers of organization, a faculty for the lucid exposition of his views and a special aptitude for managing men.' He had the unusual faculty of being equally well liked by women, for he married three times. There was, indeed, a regular Scott-Moncrieff dynasty. His nephew Georgie, also a Sapper, became in proper time Major-General Sir George and his introduction to the canals of India came in 1879, the year of the Afghan War. On disembarking at Bombay he was greeted by Mrs Ballard, 'Uncle Colin's sister' and almost certainly sib to the Ballard of Ballard's Quay. When the train stopped at Meerut he was joined by two cousins, Dr Pringle, the Inspector of Vaccinations, and Susie Willcocks, daughter to Uncle Colin's parson brother, who was married to young William Willcocks of the Indian Public Works Department. And William Willcocks' brother James was to command the Indian Corps in France in 1915. William had been born in India and received his professional education at the Roorkee College of Engineering, of which Colonel Sandes was to become Principal for many years. Colin Scott-Moncrieff, still only a Major, was Superintending Engineer of the Northern Branch of the Ganges Canal when his young nephew arrived. One of his assistants bore another famous name, famous not only within his Corps. Captain Bindon Blood, descended from that Colonel Blood who raided the Crown Jewels of Charles II, missed hardly a campaign anywhere from 1870 until the Boer War, including a turn in the Sudan against the dervishes. There were great men in the Indian service.

There were still plenty of Addiscombe men left when Colin Scott-Moncrieff worked in India. He had been born in the last year of the reign of William IV and had been destined for the Bengal Engineers from the beginning. After his time at the East India Company's school and a spell at Chatham (the Royal Engineers were well disposed to the Company and finished its young men along with their own) he arrived in India just in time for the last stages of the Mutiny. As a 22-year-old subaltern he smelt powder as galloper to Colonel Brind who was with Rose stamping out the last embers in Oudh. Exactly what happened is not entirely clear, but he carried himself well enough to earn a mention in despatches. For four or five months he lived in the saddle but with the end of the Mutiny came the end of Scott-Moncrieff's active service. Instead of chasing pandies he was given a stretch of the Western Jumna Canal to watch. This he did for two years, followed by three more on the staff of the Roorkee Civil Engineering College which bore the name of the Lieutenant-Governor in Cautley's day, Mr Thomason. In 1864 he returned to the Jumna Canal, this time in its eastern half and as full-blown Executive Engineer. After three years of this, and having learned as much as most men about canals and everything to do with them, Colin Scott-Moncrieff qualified for a long leave. He spent it in examining the canals of France, Spain and Italy. The result was a book, *Irrigation in Southern Europe, 1868,* which caught on among the professionals and made Scott-Moncrieff of the Bengal Service a known name. So much so that on his return he was given charge of the Ganges Canal at the age of 33. It was more than a matter of going round a sweetly-running machine with an oil can, for Cotton's criticisms had been demonstrated just. The main works had been neither perfectly sited nor perfectly built, resulting in too high a velocity of flow; 'Dangerous scour was consequently produced below the falls, threatening their stability. Drainage also had been neglected in the original scheme with baneful results. To remedy the defects on the main canal the falls had been remodelled in part before Moncrieff took charge, but he had to complete the remodelling of the remainder. He had also to correct the defects in alignment of the distributaries and elaborate the drainage system on sound lines'. Sir Robert Hanbury Brown, RE, who wrote this in his valediction half a century later, added 'Perhaps no lessons are so instructive and convincing as those taught by the result of mistakes made by the student himself or by others.' In time to come the lessons would be put to good use.

The rest of Scott-Moncrieff's time in India was spent in the irrigation business, ten years of it in all, broken only by the Great Famine of 1877. Madras Presidency, thanks to Cotton and his acolytes, had fared better than most places, but affairs there were being badly managed. Mysore, a princely state, was worst affected of all and much tact was needed in dealing with its rulers. Two Famine Commissioners were appointed with sweeping powers over the existing establishment. One, Charles Elliot (afterwards Lieutenant-Governor of Bengal), was in charge of finance along with the administration of camps and hospitals. The other was put to devising and supervising the Famine Relief Works; these included something like Louis Blanc's *Ateliers Nationaux,* where one set of men was put to digging ditches while a second filled them in. At least it gave work and, with work, wages. It was better than Egypt's corvée.

Scott-Moncrieff, who was named as the second Commissioner, received his marching orders soon after the arrival of his nephew George who is the authority for telling of it. 'One day in August I got a letter from Uncle Colin telling me to come to Meerut at once, as he was off to Madras and had been in Simla conferring with the authorities there as to what was to be done.' When they met, Uncle Colin 'told me that there had been difficulties in the administration of Mysore. The authorities there were not anxious to meet the Viceroy's views, and so Uncle Colin had been offered, in very flattering terms, the position of Chief Engineer for the famine relief works, a delicate post to fill for it involved his relieving and practically superseding a senior officer of engineers then holding it. I did not see my uncle again for two years, during which time he fought the famine with philanthropic energy and unquestionably saved the lives of many poor people there.' The reward of a CSI was not excessively generous. His last posting east of Suez was, by comparison, restful. The Chief Engineer, Burma, a post he held for two years, was concerned with roads, buildings, harbours and lighthouses. Such work did not stretch his professional abilities to excess.

Just before Christmas, 1882, the clock struck and Colin Scott-Moncrieff retired from the Army. To celebrate his freedom he took a last look round the old haunts. At the very end of the year he reached Lucknow and his nephew. 'I had the great pleasure of a visit from Uncle Colin and his wife and her cousin Miss Albright . . .

He spoke to me about his future, said it was strange to be his own master for the first time in his life and how, on his return to England, he proposed to take up some philanthropic work in connection with Irish immigration.' George was, perhaps, not giving this his full attention for he was captivated by Miss Albright. 'I borrowed a lady's saddle for her and mounted her on Jenny, a little mare I had recently purchased . . . The weather was delightful and we had some very pleasant gallops.' George insisted on showing the ladies all the sights of Mutiny doings in both Lucknow and Cawnpore, including 'the old church where in 1847 my Aunt Eliza had married her cousin Robert Christie. She had been married from the house of another cousin Mrs Spiers.' Within a twelvemonth both Aunt Eliza and her baby were dead. No more is heard of Miss Albright until, as Mrs Hollings, she became her uncle's biographer. She does not seem to have accompanied George on the other sentimental journey of which he speaks in his book. 'Among the places which I had officially to visit was Benares, 200 miles from Lucknow, where at that time a very big bridge was being built over the Ganges . . . it took me to a very interesting place, for it was there that my father had died in 1865. I went to see his grave and found it in very good order.' An old lady who had known George's father — and Colin's brother — told him that if 'he had taken my advice and not gone for his morning ride in a forage cap he would not have died.' More than one corner of an Indian field is for ever Scotland, and the Scott-Moncrieffs have made their contribution.

The next port of call was Paricha, near Jhansi, where young William Willcocks, who had married Susan Scott-Moncrieff, was building a weir across the Betwa. They were plainly fond of one another and a great colloquy took place about what the Scott-Moncrieffs ought to do next. The Colonel had a hankering for seeing America but he was far from being a rich man and it would certainly be expensive. March, 1883, was not the ideal moment for seeing Egypt. The Mahdi was very much on the rampage and soon the government would be assembling a ramshackle army under Hicks Pasha which would be smashed into the ground before the year was out. All the same, there was a British Army of Occupation and Egypt was always worth a visit. It had also the advantage of being much cheaper. The choice fell upon the shorter route and the two arrived at the Suez Hotel, Cairo, at the end of the same month. There a telegram was delivered. Would Colonel Scott-Moncrieff be good enough to attend upon Lord Dufferin, HM Ambassador at Constantinople and presently in Cairo advising on reform of the Egyptian government? Plainly the book on the irrigation of southern Europe must have attracted more readers than seemed likely, for the Ambassador wished to see Scott-Moncrieff in order to offer him the post of Inspector-General of Irrigation in Egypt, at an annual salary of £E2,000. Go home and think about it, he said.

Frederick Temple Hamilton-Temple-Blackwood, Marquess of Dufferin and Ava, was the kind of man whom Scott-Moncrieff would have found congenial. Though his profession of diplomat gave limited opportunities for amusement, he was great-grandson to Richard Brinsley Sheridan and had inherited much of his ancestor's wit. As Governor-General of Canada he had been an outstanding success, even to the point of persuading British Columbia not to secede from the young Federation because of broken promises over the arrival of the railway. He had been in Syria in 1860 to witness the massacre of Christians at Damascus spoken of by Macgregor, (who approved of him as a fellow member of the Royal Canoe Club), had had a seat on the International Commission set up to enquire into it and was present, as Ambassador to St Petersburg, when Czar Alexander was assassinated. Lord Dufferin had found much to admire in the Czar and wrote of 'the most useless and stupid of crimes ever recorded in history, the Liberator of the serfs of Russia.' His next posting had been to the Constantinople Embassy from which he had been uprooted to become High Commissioner for Egypt. Though he remained en poste only for a few months — moving on again to become Viceroy of India — Lord Dufferin began the work that Scott-Moncrieff and his co-adjutors were to carry out. He has never been given much credit for it.

In the nature of things there remains no record of all that passed between the two men but it is more than guesswork to take one subject for granted. Lord Dufferin knew all about serfdom in Russia and his Near Eastern experience had shown him at any rate something of what was going on in Egypt. By contrast he had seen in Canada what free men could make of an empty country. His biographer, Mr Black, knew him well and his sentiments are undoubtedly those of the Marquess. He tells of the neglected state of the canals — the delta was honey-combed with them — and the urgent need of new works. Then he tells of the 'most wasteful and oppressive system of the corvée. Five hundred men being liable to be called out for two or three weeks for work which three hundred men could finish in three days. And few of these poor creatures had picks, the majority having to delve with their own bare hands and fill the baskets with loose earth and sharp stones.' A report by an MP, an eye-witness, quoted by Lord Dufferin, describes the excavation of a canal a mile long by forty thousand men, the entire forced labour of one province: 'These poor labourers worked from sunrise to sunset, with a brief spell of rest at midday for a meal consisting of bread supplied by their relations, dipped in the water of the Nile.' For good measure, most of them suffered from ophthalmia and could hardly see what they were doing. It was nothing new. In January, 1841, Charlie Napier, Kinglake's idea of the complete naval officer, travelled by the inland waterways from Alexandria to Cairo. The canal down which his party was steaming had been, he was told, begun by Mehemet Ali in October, 1819, and finished two months later.

'The poor fellahs were driven in from the country like a flock of sheep and set to work — the greater part unprovided with tools, and all ill-fed and unpaid; exposed on a scanty allowance of water to the heat of a broiling sun by day and with little or no shelter from the noxious dews at night. Under these circumstances, it cannot be wondered that the destruction of human life was immense; but the Pacha troubled himself little about their sufferings.' Napier went on to tell of the river traffic. 'Most of the boats were the property of the Pacha, for he monopolized the greater part of the trade, as well as most of the produce of the country; and, if I may judge by their appearance, Mehemet Ali was as bad a ship's husband as he was an agriculturist . . . it is a common custom with him, when his crops are ready, to force the Fellahs to leave their own villages to work on his property. At the same time he seizes all the boats on the river to bring down his produce, caring very little what becomes of the property of others.' For all that, 'I saw no appearance of discontent or unhappiness amongst them.' Lord Dufferin's MP had noted that 'They wore felt skullcaps on their heads, exactly like those represented as the workmen in the bas-reliefs of the fourth dynasty.' They had had a lot of practice since then in bearing the almost unbearable. Given half a chance the fellah could be a good and skilful workman. Napier saw them at work in a musket factory managed by an Englishman who 'assured me of the industrious manner in which they were working . . . and I never saw so much activity in any manufactory in my life'. The hospital had schools of surgery and medicine run by a Frenchman unforgettably called Clot Bey and the students were all fellahin. His success was less than complete but it showed the right spirit. It was, however, a thing apart. Egypt, at any rate in its higher reaches, was riddled with a corruption that an Indian officer of long standing would have found hard to believe.

There was, for example, the matter of the pumps. In 1871 Linant Bey, unwilling to spend some huge sum on rebuilding the barrage, advised that steam pumps be installed throughout the Delta. The scheme slept until 1883 when Rousseau Pasha, Director of Public Works, entered into a contract with a private company to pump water from the Rosetta branch of the river into the often blocked Beheira Canal which ran through the Delta. It was to endure for 33 years, it would probably cost about £E50,000 a year and it served no purpose that the Barrage could not have served for nothing. The pumps were small portable affairs, 'owned by capitalists who sold the water. One man alone was said to be making £E15,000 a year by this means, and people like that were naturally interested in opposing any improved canalisation which would mean the spontaneous flow of water over the adjoining land'. Lord Dufferin did not admire committees. All experience showed that when some great work had to be done it was a matter of finding the right man and leaving it all to him. In Scott-Moncrieff he had found him. It may even have endeared him to the Irish peer when the engineer was suddenly offered instead the post of Financial Adviser to the Egyptian Government. Scott-Moncrieff explained that his knowledge of finance was confined to that of how to collect his own monthly pay cheque. Meantime he took Dufferin at his word and continued his journey home. At the end of April, 1883, he accepted the offer and on 3 May he was back in Egypt. Later in the same month Lord Dufferin returned to Constantinople. Management of Egyptian affairs passed to Major Baring, late RA. Evelyn Baring, grandson to the founder of the Bank, was in his early forties and at the height of his powers when he assumed the task of Pharaoh. Not everybody liked him; the adjective 'over-Baring' was irresistible to many, but, within limits, it was deserved. To one man, however, it was impossible to condescend. Colin Scott-Moncrieff had been a commissioned Sapper officer with an Indian campaign behind him when Gentleman-Cadet Baring first learned how it felt to be a 'snooker', the lowest form of animal life at The Shop. Fortunately for everybody, Colin Scott-Moncrieff was an uncommonly good-natured man.

Seniority has its advantages. When Scott-Moncrieff assumed office he laid down his terms. For six months nobody need expect to hear anything of or from him. He would need all of that time properly to appreciate the situation and to decide on what had to be done. The Under-Secretary of State for Public Works, to give him his proper title, hired a horse and a boat and disappeared from the view of officialdom. It did not take him long to find out what he was up against. The deposed Khedive Ismail had done himself very nicely, increasing his country's debt from four million Egyptian pounds to a hundred within a remarkably short time.

The money had, naturally, been spent on himself. A fine new palace at Giza remained only partially built and was cluttered up with bales of expensive French curtain material providing sustenance for destitute moths. Amongst the archives was an order for a hundred pianofortes to enable the harem ladies when under-employed to enjoy their *soirées musicaux*. Then there were his professional predecessors, both French and Egyptian. They spoke to him of the barrages. Have nothing to do with them, they counselled with one voice. The timbers were of a rottenness past believing, the ironwork was rusted, the masonry cracked. The new Under-Secretary was doubtless a man of much experience, but he did not know Egypt. Better by far to let the barrage fall to pieces, as it shortly would, and concentrate upon the installation of more and bigger pumps. The Minister Ali Pasha Mubarek, having one may imagine got little change from his new Under-Secretary, complained to the British Agent in person. With some economy of enthusiasm and under pressure from Baring he conceded that it was 27 years since his last visit. Scott-Moncrieff had learned philosophy in India. 'Happy is the reformer,' he wrote 'who finds things so bad that he cannot make a movement without making an improvement.' At the end of his six months Scott-Moncrieff had a fair idea of what he had to do. Only men in the Indian service possessed the professional ability and resistance to bribery or intimidation to carry out these works to a successful end. Baring, who had had five years as a Viceroy's secretary, knew this and was in no need of persuasion.

The second essential was to rid Egypt of the corvée and substitute a body of reasonably competent paid workmen. The first essential would be the easier. Scott-Moncrieff divided Egypt into five 'Circles', as the Holy Roman Empire had been before it. There would be three in the Delta, two in Upper Egypt and each should have a competent, Indian-experienced, engineer in charge. Within months the first two had arrived. Major Justin Ross, 'Justie' to his friends, had been an assistant engineer on various stretches of Proby Cautley's Ganges Canal since 1862. He was well regarded in his profession but his rather routine tasks that followed the actual building of the canal had given little scope for virtuosity. In 1883 his opportunity arrived. Sir Henry Lyons, for many years Director-General of the Egyptian Survey, reckoned him the real creator of modern irrigation in Egypt. His charge was irrigation of the Eastern Delta and he soon acquired an encyclopaedic knowledge of the place. This was essential in order to answer the question which propounded itself. Unless Egypt was to stagnate or even go backwards the basin system must, wherever possible, give way to irrigation from canals that would run not only at the time of high Nile but all the year round. This, if it could be effected, would bring more land under cultivation but it would demand much more water. Until the time might come when the river should be dammed high upstream, this could only be carried out by a rigid and detailed control of its flow. For the time being the Barrage was his only weapon. To derive full value from it an exact knowledge of every square mile affected was highly necessary.

Next on the scene was cousin William Willcocks, whom Colonel Sandes describes as having 'Constructive imagination amounting perhaps to genius'. He had, of course, the additional advantage of being Scott-Moncrieff's nephew by marriage.

Before treating of what the newcomers managed to do, however, it might be as well to jump ahead for a moment and consider the corvée. The word is obviously French and exactly translates the ancient practice of a more ancient France. The accompanying kurbash — the heavy whip of rhino hide used to encourage laggards — was the gift of Arab slavers. Macgregor says that even small children were not exempted from either; as soon as you could carry a basketful of stones, you were in. As no food was provided much time was lost simply in going to fetch it. And many hands do not necessarily make light work, though everybody knows what too many cooks do. The bigger landowners, of course, saw to it that their own labourers did not go; it was only those who were quite without useful friends or patrons who took up the burden. It was calculated that in 1884 the corvée furnished a slave army of 165,000 men working for 100 days. Scott-Moncrieff was by no means the only official who worked for its abolition but he was more effective than most. For a start an arrangement was cobbled up whereby a man whose number had come up could buy exemption for a season on making a small payment. The English county militias had worked in much the same way. The inevitable result was that only the very poorest and feeblest reported for duty. All manner of promises were made by Egyptian officials that the system would be abandoned but no progress was perceptible. They should not be blamed too harshly. The opposition of provincial governors, who could never have enough free labour, and what Sandes calls 'certain European Powers' was too strong for them. In February, 1887, when work on the barrage was at a particularly difficult stage, the equable Colin Scott-Moncrieff either lost his temper or affected convincingly to do so. His ultimatum went to Baring. Either the corvée ceased or he would instantly resign. Baring, though a gunner by trade, was a financier by ancestry. In concert with Nubar Pasha he found enough money to buy out the system from the Government and Egypt went the way of the American South. By 1890 all hands were free, and willing to sell their labour in the market. It was not the least of Scott-Moncrieff's claims to a nation's gratitude.

In 1883 and for a long time to come, however, the Sappers from India had to make do with things as they found them. They knew all about monsoons; they quickly learned all about the equally regular habits of their river. The task of providing Egypt with water all round the calendar instead of at immoveable feasts only would demand much more than mending the Nile Barrage, but that was their first care and the lot fell upon William Willcocks. He found little enough for his comfort. For a start the Rosetta bridge openings were every bit as bad as the local pundits had said and the Damietta openings were all lacking gates. The downstream aprons — the rough protective floors prolonging the masonry — were incomplete, the equipment deficient in everything and the staff adept only in collecting their wages. They expressed a proper solicitude for both uncle and nephew and 'their ignorance of the country so natural to foreigners'. So ignorant were they that they believed the barrage capable of salvation; or so they said. 'Tell tale' patches of cement were applied to every crack and daily examined to see whether the cracks were spreading. At the same time they took in hand making good the most obvious repairs. Their efforts were not wasted; by the time of low Nile in June, 1884, there was an extra 7 feet of water held up on the Rosetta side and nearly half that on the Damietta. Places that for years had been dry at this season found themselves flooded, the central canal — the Menufiya — had its discharge doubled and the small canals between the barrage and Cairo unexpectedly filled up. The best of it was that Baring, on the strength of this improvement, was able to borrow a cool million pounds sterling, to be applied in whatever way Scott-Moncrieff and Willcocks might think best. This was the moment of the watershed. From then on the best brains in the business could be put to work on the permanent irrigation of Egypt in the confident knowledge that it was no mere shadow-boxing. The Barrage still came first: they relieved the Rosetta branch of pressure by building a water-cushion of loose stones on the downstream floor, which enabled the work to hold back 15½ feet of water with reasonable safety. The same treatment to Damietta worked nearly as well. There were anxious moments when the old coffer-dam, which still kept the cracked and displaced portion of the Rosetta works together, partially subsided but not to any fatal extent. Thus, whilst Gordon was fighting for his life against the forces of barbarism in the last days of the Khartoum siege, others of his Corps were bringing Egypt back into the world of civilized nations from which it had long ago dropped out. The achievements of Scott-Moncrieff were so plain to be seen that he requisitioned more help from India and was given the pick of its engineers.

Justin Ross had been the first of them, one of the last Addiscombe graduates still in the service; he had served his time with the Bengal Engineers before being caught up in the post-Mutiny mass transfer to the Queen's service. If genius is really an infinite capacity for taking pains then 'Justie' Ross qualified for the word; but he would never have claimed it, nor would his contemporaries have deemed it apt. His gift was for measuring, for technical formulae and calculating the discharges needful for keeping the canals operative without silting up. His success in this was not attained without the perspiration that Thomas Edison reckoned to constitute 99 per cent of genius, for he spent the greater part of his time in Egypt stalking up and down the canal banks, stick in hand, judging the slope of a plain when it dropped only by a foot in a mile. It was widely believed that Ross carried in his head the proper upstream and downstream levels of every regulator in Lower Egypt at any time, and it was probably true. On top of this he was a likeable man with a gift for languages and the capacity for getting on with people. The men engaged on humdrum tasks would cease droning out their ancestral dirges — some British officers insisted that they all ended with same chorus of 'Ooma Ra' — to talk with Abu Nabut, the man with the stick. They needed nobody to tell them that Major Ross was a friend. But he was no longer young and could not go on for ever. There arrived in 1885, at Scott-Moncrieff's invitation, his assistant and eventual successor, the 36-year-old civilian William Drummond Garstin, late of Cheltenham — that regular purveyor of young men to the ICS — and King's College, London.

There were things going on in and to the south of Egypt in 1885 that had nothing to do with engineering but looked far more important. With Gordon engulfed at the beginning of the year it seemed to be only a matter of time before the warlike Dervishes of the Mahdi would overcome the weak Egyptian army and march to the sea. By the end of the year a strong body of them had penetrated as far as Ginnis, on the east bank of the river and a hundred miles or so south of Wady Halfa. This could not be allowed even by Mr Gladstone's short-lived government and a small army, built round the Royal Berkshires, the Camerons and the 20th Hussars, was sent to see them off; it did so very effec-tively but the snake was only scotched. Cairo was not yet as safe for wives and children as Calcutta.

It was not for reasons of security that Scott-Moncrieff forbade his assistants to live there. One of their main jobs would be to discover and root out the dirty work that was certainly afoot on the part of officials and landlords of the kind his Indian men would call zemindars. Scott-Moncrieff was not always kindly Uncle Colin. When the Egyptian Government demurred at such an idea he told it firmly that if his wishes were not respected he would send all his people back to India. He was absolutely right. Inspectors popping up without warning and in the most unlikely places worked wonders.

There were other reasons why Cairo was not a desirable home for the irrigation men. William Garstin found it out. In 1888, after he had served some time on the Barrage, he met in the city the young Mary North, a cousin of the Earl of Guilford. Miss North (who ever after maintained that she was only in Cairo because her chaperone believed her to be the Earl's sister) was nineteen and had no money. Mr Garstin did not rank high in society. Miss North, though not affecting even to like him — she found him pompous beyond anything she had known — agreed to be his wife and bore him two children. It was her misfortune to encounter in Cairo society that famous dazzler of little girls, Major Charles à Court, with whom she eventually bolted. Bolting wives are not invariably their husband's fairest judges and, many year later, Mary Repington (à Court's new name) wrote unkindly of him as 'stern and cold'. She also claimed to have found out the reason Will Garstin married her. 'Sir Colin Scott-Moncrieff was an old man. His successor as Under-Secretary for Public Works would be chosen from the four men he had brought from India with him. Three of them were married. They had married young, and their wives were middle-aged, middle-class women — no particular assets to a gay cosmopolitan society like Cairo.' It was a point of view. There is a glimpse of Scott-Moncrieff which deserves to survive. 'I liked Sir Colin very much indeed, and as I reminded him of a beloved daughter who had died, he was very fond of me. He was, as his name implies, a Scot and a deeply religious man, with a rather more emotional temperament than is often found in one of his stock. He used to read the lessons in church on Sunday, a fact that Will would refer to viciously whenever he was angry with him.' There was much to be said for the economy of living in the bush, even though 'the Locke-Kings, whose fine house, Ockham, was built almost on the lines of a solid English mansion, gave the most delightful parties'. They could afford them. The Locke-Kings owned the Mena House Hotel.

The other Indian men recruited by Scott-Moncrieff were two Sapper officers. Major James Western was late of the Bengal Engineers and a contemporary of Justin Ross; his experience also was on Cautley's Ganges Canal where he had ended up at Paricha building a new Betwa Canal with Willcocks serving under him. Proby Cautley may have come off worse than Cotton in India but his disciples in Egypt surely levelled the score. Captain Robert Hanbury Brown was a dozen years younger and with a great reputation waiting to be made. The civilian element came from Mr Reid and Mr Foster, along of course, with Mr Garstin.

Scott-Moncrieff allotted them their tasks. Western and Reid were to be responsible for the Barrage along with Willcocks. Very properly the Sapper officers had salaries of £E1500 a year against £E1000 to the civilians. The latter had longer careers in front of them. To begin, they needed to decide whether it was practical politics to continue patching up the existing Barrage or whether to scrap and replace it. There was only one way to find out. The floor, presently under 15½ feet of water, must somehow be exposed and inspected. The job could only be done, if it could be done at all, during the period of low Nile and it must not interfere with the holding-up of water whilst being done. Scott-Moncrieff, reasonably enough, said that it was like trying to mend a watch without stopping it. The results were interesting. A high wall of earth banked off twenty arches at the western end of the Rosetta arm and for once the pumps came in useful. The floor was exposed, the cracks in both floors and arches were plainly serious and borings showed that even at 200 feet there was no rock foundation. Though it did not look promising the work was not impossible. In order to prevent its undermining by water they decided to adopt Indian practice and spread the foundation out very wide. They doubled the width of the old floor from 112 feet to 224, covered it with a mass of concrete and stonework 3 feet thick and then prolonged it in both directions. Along the upstream edge they drove a line of sheet-piling 16 feet deep. If water could percolate under all that it would be remarkable indeed. Then, just below the bridge, they sank the heavy blocks of dressed stone brought from the Alps. Because of the ticking watch factor it was not possible to shut off either branch completely; this meant that only one half of each could be treated during successive low Niles, or four years work. And that is exactly how it happened. On 16 June, 1890, the team reported that all was done and the last embankment could be removed. Colonel Sandes was able to say that when the Nile is at its lowest in May and June the whole of the water is poured on to the fields and none whatever escapes to the sea.

In point of timing things had worked out rather well. The Barrage was of the greatest importance but it provided no sort of reservoir and no insurance against a bad season. It was accepted on all sides that a dam of some kind would have to be built far upstream but the last few years had not been propitious. Ever since Gordon died in Khartoum the Mahdi and his successor the Khalifa had been determined to carry the Dervish revolution into the land of Egypt; nor was this idea an absurdity, for a peasants' revolt under the whip of religion was never impossible. British officers looking south through their glasses from the walls of Wady Halfa felt themselves at one with the centurions on another wall who had peered north into the mists and wondered when the Picts would come. South of Halfa was nothing but ancient chaos, with tales of frightful cruelty coming out from time to time. The fight at Ginnis in '85 had put an end to the possibility of an immediate follow-up operation but it was no secret that some day the hordes of camel-borne sword and spearmen would be back. In the summer of 1889 the storm broke. Wad-al-Najumi, very much a desert general to be reckoned with, erupted from outer space and offered battle at the village of Argin, to the north of Wady Halfa. Civilization was ready for him. The three Sudanese battalions of the Egyptian Army, having scores of their own to settle, were as good for this kind of work as any infantry on earth. Three old Shop men were at the head of it. Jocelyn Wodehouse, late RA, commanded the Division. Mary Garstin's regular dancing partners were well represented, 'Hal' Rundle conducting the voice of the guns and 'Taffy' Lewis leading the best of the Sudanese. At the last fight at Toski, almost in the shadow of Abu Simbel, the officer commanding the cavalry brigade was soon to be the most famous Sapper of them all. He was not one of the partners, for Mary was terrified of him. 'The only two women in whose company he seemed to take pleasure, or with whom he apparently found any topics of conversation whatsoever during the ten years or so that I saw him constantly were Mrs Clinton Dawkins and the handsome dark-eyed niece of his great friend Pandeli Ralli — Miss Evelyn Morton who subsequently married General Sir Julian Byng'. Even more fearsome was 'a very severe looking lady, his sister'. Millie Parker, mother to the young man mentioned in the Introduction, had nothing of common ground with Mary, the flighty young wife of the ambitious engineer.

Kitchener Pasha was no Rupert but his Brigade did all that was demanded of it. Toski was the Dervish Gettysburg, for the day ended with Wad-al-Najumi dead on his sheepskin and his forces scattered. Never again would the brave sword and spearmen reduce the overfed Pashas of Cairo to a jelly of fear; the days of the Dervishes were numbered, the reconquista would shortly begin and the engineers could give single-minded attention to their work. There would be no peasants' revolt, although nine more years were to pass before Kitchener took the war to the Sudan for the last time and stood bare-headed where Gordon had died.

With that over it was opportune to think seriously about conserving rather than re-distributing water. As long ago as 1866 Sir Samuel Baker, in a letter to *The Times*, had floated the idea of a dam at Aswan. Scott-Moncrieff, invited to consider all possibilities, deputed both Colonel Western and William Willcocks to investigate and report. Though more than one possibility was mooted the plan finally adopted for construction of the first Aswan Dam was drawn up jointly by Willcocks and Garstin and they accepted all responsibility when it came to be built. Eminent in their profession both these gentlemen were, but they had the misfortune not to be Sappers and therefore have no further place in this book.

Colin Scott-Moncrieff retired from the Egyptian service in 1892, still only 56 and active. Mary Garstin knew him fairly well and, whether or not he knew of her private affairs, he always stood her friend. 'Soon after I first knew him Sir Colin married his third wife, a gentle and well-endowed Quaker lady, much younger than himself and with surprisingly modern ideas.' Mary became a regular visitor at their house in Cheyne Walk, apparently even after she had dropped out of society in 1900. His long twilight — he died in 1916 — was kept busy. Knighthood came with retirement, along with a spell in Central Asia advising the Czar's government on the irrigation of Merv in Turkmenistan. The city, standing by an oasis, had been founded by Alexander the Great, used for centuries by Persian monarchs as their capital and had been destroyed by an earthquake in 1794. By 1884 it had just become a part of All the Russias and a completely new town was built. Scott-Moncrieff's reward was worth more to posterity than many pages in the DNB. The Mess at Chatham holds as one of its great treasures — and it has many — the magnificent silver-gilt and enamel punch-bowl presented by the Czar himself.

On retirement Scott-Moncrieff became once more caught up in the affairs of backward countries as Under Secretary for Scotland. Four years later he was back in his beloved India as Chairman of the Irrigation Commission, a post that called for visits rather than permanent residence. This brought him a belated KCSI. A brother sapper who had worked much with him in Egypt, Major Sir

Robert Hanbury Brown, remarked in a memoir that 'there had been one long-sustained battle which Sir Colin had set his heart on winning'. Much later, 'The victory was won at last and the Corvee lay dead'. *The Dictionary of National Biography* does not rate Colin Campbell Scott-Moncrieff worth a mention.

One last piece of sapper work, however, demands one. In the Kitchener Papers at the Public Record Office is the plan of a new Khartoum, to be built on the site of the razed pest-house that had stood there. In the centre stands the statue of General Gordon on his camel. Round him are roads and streets in the exact shape of the Union flag. Thus Sir Herbert Kitchener left it, as a warning to any future Mahdis or Khalifas. It is a pity that when the motor-car arrived the plan had to be modified in order to allow drivers to go round corners. But it was a message firmer than anything on a Pharaonic cartouche for so long as it lasted. The last contribution by the greatest of Sappers had nothing to show but was none the less serviceable. In 1899, under his peremptory orders, a permanent channel was cut through the sudd; it was Garstin's work. Scott-Moncrieff's barrage was the last substantial contribution by the Royal Engineers to the building of a nervous system for civilization. With the new century came the civilian contractors, Sir John Aird whose firm built the first Aswan Dam to Willcock's designs, Weetman Pearson, who became Viscount Cowdray after building Dover Harbour, and the rest of them. And with the civilians came the unions and civilian-mindedness. Nothing in that world would be quite the same again.

VIII

Prisons, Promenade Concerts
And The Arts Of Peace

THE PRISONS OF ENGLAND have never been a source of great national pride. Until fairly modern times it did not matter all that much. Everybody convicted of almost any crime was hanged with some promptitude and made little demand upon the accommodation available. Though such exemplary justice relieved overcrowding in the gaols the temper of later ages disapproved and reforming men, among whom the name of John Howard must forever stand first, adumbrated the view that convicts were human. Even more eccentrically, so were debtors. The early enthusiasts for prison reform were unable to achieve much. When it came, it was through the instrumentality of a Sapper officer.

It began through a strange concatenation of events. In 1829 the British Government decreed that the westernmost part of the Australian continent be created a Colony, under the name of the Swan River. This was to be no mere convict settlement but a better class of province altogether, much as Edward Gibbon Wakefield had planned during his own imprisonment. Land was to be sold cheaply to respectable families and they should be encouraged to bring servants and settle down in proper English fashion. Since Swan River Colony was little more than a name on a map it could hardly have come as a surprise that convicts had to be imported from other parts of the continent to provide the labour to build everything that needed building; and to stand guard over the convicts while they worked a garrison was needed. Again it should hardly have surprised anybody that, for a long time, growth into something recognisable as a piece of England overseas was not swift.

The temper at home was an odd one, for a belief had grown up that, with some 13 million people living in England and probably about another 9 million in Ireland, the country was over-populated. When the call went out in 1820 for respectable people willing to make new homes in South Africa, they were officially designated 'the redundant population'. Two other factors were at work. The Colonies were at last beginning to have had enough of being used as spoil-heaps for the criminal classes and were beginning to say so out loud. The Irish potato famine had created a substantial class of people technically convicts because they had been sentenced for crime but factually perfectly decent and driven to petty offences simply by hunger. By the late 1840s the authorities were seeking to cast their net wider. A shipload was sent to Bermuda, where the Governor declined to accept them. Next they were shipped to Cape Town, where an Anti-Convict Association sprang into being overnight and petitioned its Governor to send them packing. He has already made more than one appearance in this book, for Sir Harry Smith, though a Rifleman, saw as much of the world as any Sapper. He put down something much like a riot, whipped up by the Association, and offered his own resignation. Lord Grey saw that South Africa was unavailable and the miserable Irish sailed on the Tasmania.

At that point the Sapper involvement begins.. Edmund Yeamans Walcott Henderson, born at Deal as befitted an Admiral's son, had passed out of The Shop in 1838 at the age of 17 and had been six years in Canada, working as one of the commissioners marking out the boundary between New Brunswick and the outermost limits of the USA. If that were not occupation enough for a subaltern, he had the task of deciding whether or not a railway line of 700 miles, linking the Maritimes with the line from Halifax to Quebec, was practicable. Henderson was given the western half of New Brunswick, in which he was fortunate; Captain Pipon, who had been allotted the eastern, was swept from his canoe in the Restigouche Rapids and was drowned. The task was much like that in British Columbia, but there was no Hudson's Bay Company upon whose experience men could draw. Henderson wrote, 40 years later, of the difficulty in surveying mighty forests completely unknown to anybody except the lumbermen who worked them. None the less, he made an excellent report, complete with panoramic sketch, of the country, which came to the notice of Lord Grey. Though it sounds a non sequitur, the Colonial Secretary was so taken by the quality of Henderson's work in the woods that he offered the young man — he was still only 29 — the appointment of Comptroller of Convicts in Western Australia. He explained that the Swan River Colony had not fulfilled everybody's hopes, largely because of the shortage of labour. For that reason, and because the older Colonies in the East were now flatly refusing to take any more convicts, a penal settlement was to be set up. In addition, the Government would send out one free emigrant for each felon; these last should no longer be gaol-sweepings but men selected for their apparent ability to measure up to colonial life; after a spell in prison on arrival they would either be put to constructing new public works or sent out to private employers under police supervision.

It all sounded wise and far-seeing. Henderson had the credential of bringing with him the wife he had married in Halifax and who herself had the advantage of being born a Murphy. They disembarked at Fremantle in June, 1850, to find, as might have been expected, that nobody knew anything about them. Fortunately somebody had had the good sense to make up the convict escort from the Royal Engineers. Henderson, having sent back a requisition for more, put them to work at building for themselves a prison, a barracks and all that go with such things. In due time help came, in the shape of the 20th Company RE, under Captain Wray. Captain Wray went to his grave a Major-General, his second-in-command ended as Colonel Sir William Crossman but it is neither of these distinguished officers who continue the story. The third, and most junior, carries it on.

Edmund Frederick Du Cane, RE, was about as unlikely a man to become a prison reformer as can easily be imagined. His ancestry was part Huguenot settled in Essex and part Irish; his father had been an officer of light cavalry in the Peninsula and his mother had been one of the Wares of Mallow. Dedham Grammar School passed him on at 13 to a Wimbledon crammer who secured him a place at The Shop when he was 16 and the year was 1846. Young Gentlemen Cadet Du Cane soon grew to his full 6 feet 4 and his particular talent seemed to be for making comic and often indecorous sketches of his friends. This was not incompatible with having an excellent brain and he passed out in 1848 at the head of his batch. Du Cane was an uncommonly handsome young fellow with an inherited fluency in French. This resulted in his being taken at the age of 20 from his Sapper company at Chatham in order to have some hand in interesting Louis Napoleon in Prince Albert's Great Exhibition. His full title was 'Assistant Superintendent of the Foreign Side of the International Exhibition and Assistant Secretary to the Jury of Awards'. What exactly his duties were has been obscured by time, but one event is recorded with certainty. Louis Napoleon, still only Prince-President but meditating the coup-d'etat of 2 December, invited Du Cane and the others forming the Exhibition staff to stay as his guests at the Tuileries. It is a thousand pities that no record has survived. Du Cane, as his Australian caricatures show, was a compulsive sketcher and the targets in Paris of 1851 must have been as irresistible as they were unending. Nothing remains and as soon as he returned to Chatham Du Cane was brought down to earth with a posting to Western Australia. His many shipboard drawings certainly suggest that he enjoyed the voyage.

Still only 21, the Roman age of maturity at which a man could bear the weight of armour, Edmund Du Cane found himself in command of a large force of convicts condemned to build themselves a home. Though details of their daily labours are scanty, and would not make absorbing reading, it is plain that they built well. *The Daily Telegraph* for 6 January, 1988, contains a report from 'Our Perth Correspondent' that speaks to the durability of the work. It tells of how 130 prisoners in Fremantle jail (the American spelling is to be deprecated, but cannot be avoided) 'held 5 warders hostage and stranded others on a wall for nearly 20 hours as the temperature reached 108 Fahrenheit'. It goes on to recount how 'The rioters then set fire to the archaic prison which was built by convicts in 1855'. The Chaplain, yet another of the great clan McGregor, explained that the Royal Commission had declared the prison inadequate as far back as 1898. As elsewhere, sappers built to last.

Work was also carried out in building a home for Lieutenant Du Cane, a fine bungalow at the new village of Guildford. There were, however, lighter moments, perpetuated by his sketches and cartoons. One is a specimen of potted philosophy. A brother officer, languidly exquisite and flanked by a variety of livestock and a young woman in a crinoline, bears a motto. 'He that is rich and wants to be poor, Let him keep a gamecock, a race-horse and ★★★★★'. It sounds like the voice of experience. This would have come early, for by the time he was not quite 24 Du Cane had been appointed a Magistrate of the Colony and Visiting Magistrate of Convict Stations. Just as he was settling into becoming a considerable expert in these matters a ship arrived summoning him home, like most other RE officers in distant places, to do duty in the Crimea★. By the time his ship reached Falmouth it was June, 1856, and the war was long over. Du Cane, on orders, joined the department of the Inspector-General of Fortifications in Pall Mall and, like other of his kind, was caught up in Lord Palmerston's fortifying of the south coast against any possible onfall by Du Cane's former host, now Emperor Napoleon III. In this he continued for the better part of the next seven years.

Once more his activities demonstrate how much, and how important, was the contribution made by very young and very junior sapper officers to the defence of the Realm in addition to their more civilian activities in what were then reasonably called outposts of Empire. After a couple of years on docks and harbours Du Cane was assigned in 1858 to the building of new land works at Dover (where, of course, no harbour would exist until forty years later) and on the ring of forts covering Plymouth, from Fort Staddon to the Tamar.

While he was engaged amongst the mamelons, ravelins, caponieres and suchlike, the prison system was beginning to take some rudimentary shape. Of the great Napoleonic prisoner-of-war camps at Norman Cross and Dartmoor only the buildings of the latter remained standing and were kept steadily filled by a new generation of miscreants. The first model penitentiary, Pentonville, itself designed by Lt.-Colonel Joshua Jebbe, RE, had opened for business in 1842; its object was to keep inmates busy at something useful like picking oakum or building up their muscles on the

★ For an account of his Australian days, see *Royal Engineer: A Life of Sir Edmund Du Cane* by Alexandra Husluck. Published by Angus & Robertson 1973.

treadmill* rather than staring miserably at the wall. Little Dorrit's Marshalsea, a feature of Southwark High Street since the reign of Edward III, was pulled down three years after Pentonville opened. The even older Newgate still crouched disreputably where the Central Criminal Court now stands and the debtors' establishments remained much as they had been for many decades. By the early 1860s, however, crime, criminals and all that went with them had become modish. One reason was that the Colonies, or those of them whose hospitality towards the criminal classes had long been taken for granted, had had enough and were saying so.

And it was under Lord Palmerston, however unlikely it may seem, that the reforms were put in hand. In 1861 came the string of Acts reforming the criminal law, many of which still form the basis of it. Four years later came the Prison Act of 1865, giving wide powers of regulation to the Home Secretary. In between the two, Captain Edmund Du Cane became once more caught up in the newly invented subject, or science, of penology. Of one thing he was already sure; being a convict in Western Australia was not heaven on earth, but the open air life in a superior climate had to be a thousand times better than existence in a London slum with a choice between stealing and starving. There was nothing mawkish in this. The Victorian rough, as Du Cane did not need to be told, could be as ugly a customer as existed anywhere. Many could only be improved by hanging, but the majority were not fiends and deserved to be treated like grown men.

Du Cane's involvement in it all happened through the agency of Edmund Henderson. When he became appointed Chairman of the Board of Directors of Convict Prisons he needed a deputy. No superior talent or philosophy being found among the available candidates, Henderson sent for his old subordinate and offered him the job; its full title was 'Director of Convict Prisons and Inspector of Military Prisons'. Du Cane, who now had a genuine interest in the subject and had already seen something of colonial prisons, accepted. Whether he then realised that, at 33, he had stumbled upon the work for which he was designed it is

---

* Another of East Anglia's aids to gracious living. Cubitt had invented it in 1817 and the 'Ipswich Treadmill' soon spread throughout the Houses of Correction.

not possible to say with any confidence. Certainly he spent the next year and a half acquainting himself with every detail of the old system of penal servitude as it was before the Act. There seemed plenty of room for improvement.

Transportation finally came to an end in 1867. Two years later Du Cane succeeded Henderson as Chairman of the Board of Directors of convict prisons, Surveyor-General of prisons, Inspector-General of military prisons and, in case this were not enough, he was given charge of all colonial prisons. His army rank was still Captain.

One idea was always at the front of Du Cane's mind. The convict, so far as possible, should earn his keep and not merely build muscle by daily treadmill exercise. In this way he furnished a disciplined and inexpensive labour corps for the construction of Portsmouth and Chatham Docks as well as the defence works on Portland Bill. Then came the matter of local prisons. There were many of these, varying from village lock-ups and roundhouses of respectable antiquity to fairly modern fortresses fit to house dangerous men. There was no central authority. Everyone was rudely administered by the local Justices and their clerks. In all there were something like 2,000 of them, each dependent upon local rates for its upkeep and existence. By 1873 Du Cane had drawn up a plan for the transfer of all this miscellany to the central government which would administer, and pay for, the whole.

In July, 1877, Mr Disraeli's government passed the plan into law.

Du Cane, now Brevet-Colonel, was given his reward, a KCB. The number of prisons was cut by half, a regular prison staff brought into being with a regular promotion structure, uniform rules set out for all prisons and the whole prison world was reborn on Army lines. His abiding memorial is neither town, lake nor river; at the back of Wormwood Scrubs Prison, largely his creation, runs Du Cane Road. It is a form of immortality, even if a slight one.

Sir Edmund, once he had got his teeth into the subject, also tackled the prevention and detection of crime. The first Commissioner of Police (jointly with Richard Mayne, whose son we met in British Columbia) had been Colonel Charles Rowan, late 52nd Regiment and one of the Duke's best Peninsula officers.

For a long time he had opposed the idea of a separate Detective Division but by the early 1870s, after much experience, he was changing his view. The Criminal Investigation Department of the Metropolitan Police began operations in 1877. During the same year Du Cane made a useful contribution to its work by causing his convicts to print the first 'Black Book'. It contained a register of something over 12,000 habitual criminals, complete with aliases, habits and methods of working. Sir Edmund, like many another man, was persuaded that criminals had a recognisable cast of countenance. He went further than Lombroso, for he began to wonder, along with Francis Galton, whether there could really be anything in the theory of finger-prints. Galton, ultimately Sir Francis, was convinced and interested himself. A further Register followed, this time including each criminal's distinctive marks. The time for fingerprints was not quite yet.

The machine set up by Du Cane ran fairly smoothly and much of it remains today. By the curious system of the time his promotion continued steadily in the Army List although it was long since he had seen service. On the last day of the Jubilee year, 1887, he was promoted Major-General on his retirement from the Army and in March, 1895, he left the public service completely.

Photographs of Edmund Du Cane in middle life show a handsome man with his face fimbriated in the high Victorian fashion. It is a good-natured face, that of a man happy in his work and at ease with life. This should not be surprising. Apart from being a considerable expert on Napoleonic literature he was a good artist, good enough to have his Peninsular sketches exhibited at the Chelsea Show of 1890. Like so many retired Sapper officers he became a mighty contributor to the correspondence columns of *The Times* and the magazines published a number of his articles on prison reform. It seems odd that so merry a man should have devoted most of his working life to a subject so dismal but it does furnish another example of the catholicity, as well as the ubiquity, of his Corps.

There is a tedious pleasantry, wearily resented by each passing generation, that all Sapper officers are 'mad, married, or Methodists'. The first and last can be taken as the schoolboy ruderies they are, but there must once have been something in the second. Colonel Kitchener, father of the Field Marshal and an old cavalryman, wrote about it to his daughter when she sought advice about her son's career. The Colonel did not recommend The Shop. 'If he gets into the Engineers and does not, as Herbert did, get out of it which very few do, his duties are not over-pleasant, he is very much by himself and if with other officers they are generally married. The consequence of their being so often separated from other people.' He then added, nastily, 'Moreover, I do not think they are as a rule acceptable to the other branches of the service'.* Mr Henry Cole, when writing his 'Brief Notes on the late Captain Francis Fowke' in 1866 took something of the same view. It should have caused no surprise. Mr Cole , even after he became Sir Henry, remained a dedicated bachelor; he is also reputed to have introduced the Christmas card to England. He told of Fowke's birth in Belfast in 1823, of his early education in Ireland and of his passing out from The Shop in 1842. Then follows the accusation: 'He was only just of age when he fulfilled that destiny which seems so common to young Engineer officers, and took to himself a wife. He married Miss Rede, and soon after this event was sent out to Bermuda.' If this was the worst his Colonel could do for Fowke it could hardly be punishment.

Neither of the services set itself out to encourage matrimony, especially among young officers. The Navy rather prides itself on a famous letter, addressed in 1793 to Lieutenant Bayntun. 'Sir, You having thought fit to take to yourself a wife are to look for no further attentions from, Your Humble Servant, J. Jervis'. As the letter, misdirected by Lady Jervis — this was before her lord became St. Vincent — was to an officer whose mind had never for a moment been clouded by an idea so infamous the reply was unsurprising. Lieutenant Bayntun, 'in all astonishment', ventured to ask the Admiral 'who could have so traduced him, for that he abhorred the idea as much as Sir John did'. Forgiven, he lived to become an Admiral himself. His nasty experience, however, underlined the point. Marriage was for civilians; no exception could be made for a technical Corps. If young Sapper officers

---

* Lord Kitchener's nephew, discouraged by this, joined the Royal Sussex and eventually became famous as Parker Pasha of Sinai. His grandfather's letter appears in full in *The Diaries of Parker Pasha,* Quartet Books, 1983, p.24.

defied the conventions they must expect taunts. Fowke's duties in the West Indies do not seem to have been onerous. Mr Cole himself says that his young friend and his Louisa spent most of their time in and on the water as a sensible couple should. It was in Bermuda that their son Frank, in due time Assistant Secretary to the Board of Education, was born. His father 'seems to have excited attention by numerous clever devices for the rigging of a canvass (sic) Yacht'. Mr Cole was not well informed about pleasure sailing. If, as seems likely, he meant that Fowke enjoyed messing about with boats that would fold up it would not be the last time.

Fowke was one of those men of insatiable curiosity who could never be entirely happy without inventing things or improving upon the inventions of other people. His first posting once back home provided a little scope. Raglan Barracks at Devonport needed rebuilding and Fowke, still a subaltern, was given the work do to. It was his first essay into architecture and, says Mr Cole, 'he introduced, not without opposition, many useful novelties conducive to the health and comfort of soldiers, which are now accepted as necessary in Barrack accommodation'. This was a couple of years before the public knew of the existence of Miss Nightingale; she and Fowke clearly worked on the same lines though independently. A moment's pause might be used to consider the architect in Britain during this time. Architecture was not recognized as a profession. The purists hold that there were only five of these: the Navy, the Army, the Church, Medicine and the Law. Until as recently as 1931 anybody could style himself architect, nail up a plate and do his worst. There were no schools in Britain devoted to the teaching of architecture and cognate subjects and the best instruction available was to be had at The Shop.

Fowke had a talent for it. He had been saved from a life of service to the guns only by the excellence of his drawing — 'a fact worth recollection by all those who desire to be Engineers' — and the standard was a high one. For the moment, however, he occupied his leisure with his inventions. There was an elongated shot for rifled ordnance, but nobody would even give it a try. His 'collapsing pontoons' deserved to fare better. Nobody took the smallest interest in them during Fowke's lifeime, though it was rumoured that they were used successfully during the American Civil War. They were already quite old then, for Fowke had shown them in two sizes at the Paris Exhibition of 1855. The smaller model exactly resembled the infantry assault craft of Hitler's War; the canvas-sided folding pontoon had much in common with the D. D. Sherman tanks that swam bravely ashore on 'D' Day. Fowke, here, was unlucky. Many of the improvements in equipment long taken for granted — they include the bicycle, the machine-gun and the motor-car — were first taken up by the richer Volunteer Corps. If they proved worth while, the Army took them over. The First Middlesex Volunteer Engineers bought a number of them and tried them out.

This Corps, the first of its kind, for Volunteers had seldom found engineering to their taste, had been raised by Fowke. Their drill shed, designed by him and measuring 100 feet by 40, cost only £100. Sir Joseph Paxton, of Crystal Palace fame, remarked to Mr Cole that it was the cheapest thing of its kind he had ever seen. The principle of its construction, he tells us, was copied throughout the country, and not only for drill-sheds. It worked equally well for conservatories. Captain Fowke has a fair claim to have been the direct ancestor of all the Field Squadrons and Companies of the Engineers of the Territorial Army. Their feats in the world wars are, or ought to be, common knowledge to everyone.

The collapsible pontoons, however, did not catch on, for the army in the Crimea had no need of such things. Once that war was over any interest there might have been tailed off.

It was the Paris Exhibition that set Fowke on the track he was to follow. Though nobody wanted his folding boats or his drawbridge it brought about, quite by chance, a meeting with his brother Sapper, Colonel Owen, who was its secretary. Owen had a high opinion of his junior and invited him to help in superintending the Machinery Department of the Exhibition. Sir William Reid, who was much involved, may have had a hand in this. When Owen was summoned back to do proper sapper work in front of Sebastopol, Fowke succeeded to the secretaryship. It meant spending a year in the Paris of Napoleon III, something that he and the other young RE officers similarly circumstanced were able to contemplate with equanimity. Being a married man he was not tempted away from his work as others may have been. Evidence of this remains. Captain Fowke conducted numerous and valuable experiments on the strengths of a variety of colonial woods. His conclusions were published in the Parliamentary Report on the Exhibition and put out as a pamphlet under the title 'Civil Construction'. This did not occupy all Fowke's time. He also drew up a report on all the exhibits of a seafaring turn under the heading 'Naval Construction' and for his many pains he was awarded the Legion of Honour. As it was only the civil version Captain Fowke was not allowed to wear it.

Mr Cole (he received his 'K' on retirement in 1875) was a man of some distinction when he and Fowke first met in 1854. His main interest in life was the preservation of public records and he has a better claim than any other man to the honour of forcing an uninterested government to set up the Public Record Office. Apart from his hobby of writing railway guide books under the aestival name of Felix Summerly, he devoted most of his half century of service to the business of museums, in addition to art manufacture, art designs, art schools, art everything, including as his obituarist unkindly adds 'sometimes art vulgarisation'. He had, inevitably, had much to do with the Great Exhibition, from which he moved on to the one at Paris where Napoleon III was demonstrating the French superiority in all things. It was in Paris that he met Captain Fowke. After Fowke's death Cole wrote that he had 'a sluggish and indolent temperament, though he could be roused to prompt action occasionally'. It was hardly generous; the remainder of Fowke's short life was to have quite a number of notable achievements crammed into it. To begin with, when his Parisian period was over, Fowke was posted as an Inspector to the Science and Art Department, then quartered in Marlborough House. He was also, at the instance of John Fox Burgoyne, made one of the Commissioners of the International Technical Commission whose business it was to find out how the St George's branch of the River Danube might be made navigable. On this subject Mr Cole seems less well informed than usual. His assertion that Fowke's scheme 'was unanimously adopted' came in for flat contradiction from others who knew better. Fowke and the

Danube were not closely acquainted; that is hardly surprising, even making no allowance for the sluggish and indolent aspect. There was work nearer home to keep him up to the collar.

For a start, he designed the interiors of both the Dublin National Gallery and the Museum of Science and Art at Edinburgh. Either simultaneously or very nearly so he was set to work on organizing the new home, at South Kensington, for his own Department.

There was certainly room for improvement. When Brompton was a suburb (the coincidence of name with the Royal Engineers' barracks is fortuitous) there had been a 'nest of old houses' — Mr Cole's words — of a faintly disreputable kind. Their owners were, or had been, Sir Cresswell Cresswell, the Judge who is still remembered as the creator of the Divorce Court and of which he became in 1857 the first President. He had the misfortune, rare amongst Judges, to be killed in a carriage accident. Next to him in the nest was Mr Greenwood, senior partner of Cox and Greenwood, the Army Agents. Being bank manager to almost every serving officer, from the Commander-in-Chief down, he had been the recipient of many requests for favours. To one he had certainly acceded. 'The Duke of York was accustomed to retire to Mr Cox's house for a change of air,' is how Mr Cole puts it. There is no mention of Mrs Mary Ann Clark. Whether or not the tone was raised by the third owner, 'Madame Celeste', can no longer be ascertained. By the time Fowke came on the scene the houses were riddled with dry rot and had to go, along with the iron shed known as The Boilers built by Sir William Cubitt himself. Cubitt, who ought to have been a Sapper, has many claims to fame, varying from Cardiff Docks and Rochester Bridge to the prison treadmill, adapted from the Chinese and set up at Brixton in 1817. All the buildings were swept away in order to make a site for the South Kensington Museum. Mr Cole was appointed its first Director. The Boilers, designed as an Iron Museum, ended up at Bethnal Green some years later, leaving parts of their structure incorporated into the new building.

All this activity did not inhibit Captain Fowke from inventing more useful artefacts. There was a 'very portable fire-engine', adopted by the Army; a collapsing camera and a bath that would pack up like a book; an improved umbrella, so constructed that all its parts should be contained within the thickness of an ordinary walking stick, that proved impossible to make; and a lighting machine ('used throughout the Kensington Museum') which would ignite some hundreds of gas burners within seconds. The Prince Consort's Library at Aldershot was entirely of his designing. One other project, never executed, might bear dusting off. In the *Cornhill Magazine* (No 3, March, 1860) appeared suggestions for the enlargement of a building presently the subject of some interest. The article is headed 'National Gallery Difficulty Solved'.

Much of Fowke's work went into museums and picture galleries, sometimes in concert with 'Mr Redgrave, RA, who had discovered the right formula for a top-light gallery'. His particular talent, once more in the words of Mr Cole, was for 'solving the problem of the decorative use of iron and by appreciating the spirit both of the Gothic and Renaissance architects was on the threshold of introducing a novel style of architecture when, alas, death, at the early age of 42 years, has cut short his promising career'.

Had he lived only a little longer Fowke would have had a more considerable share in building the Albert Hall than came his way. Certainly much of the groundwork was carried out by him but the execution and supervision was necessarily the task of others. His chef d'oeuvre was the South Kensington Museum, now largely swallowed up by Sir Aston Webb's V & A. For those interested, there is a huge volume in the RE Corps Library containing photographs of every step in the work, from clearing The Boilers and the rest to the final stages. The strange thing, on first looking through them, is how modern everything seems. It is not merely the high quality of the prints; Cromwell Road, its people and their methods of work look substantially unchanged save only for the hansom cabs and absent motor traffic. The Museum is Fowke's memorial, for he died there in his office chair on 4 December, 1865. Overwork had brought about chest trouble; a spell in Switzerland failed to cure it and only two days after his return a blood-vessel broke. 'He was greatly beloved and was not known to have made a single enemy.'

The Albert Hall, more even than Brighton Pavilion, deserves Sydney Smith's apophthegm that 'it has a strange monstrous beauty; like the hindquarters of an elephant'. Whatever its shortcomings, London would never be the same without it. The Last Night of the Proms anywhere else would be unthinkable. Once again London has the Royal Engineers to thank. On the sudden death of Captain Fowke the torch passed into the hand of his friend Captain Henry Young Darracott Scott, then in his early 40s. At that point in his career Scott's main claim to eminence was that he had invented hachuring, the system of representing heights on maps by sketching designs that resemble fishbones. Fowke had already completed most of the drawing work; Scott's task was to supervise the construction. It was no sort of sinecure.

The great feature of the Albert Hall was to be its domed roof. Domes, certainly domes of that size, were not familiar things in England. Everybody knew of the great dome erected by the Emperor Justinian over his church of Santa Sophia at Constantinople; how, after standing for forty years, it suddenly crashed to the ground in the year 558. Justinian had certainly caused it to be rebuilt and it was still standing in 1870, but Justinian, as everybody knows, had had the advantage of angels directing his building work. Lacking that, Scott demonstrated a considerable faith in his own skill and the workmanship of his contemporaries. When the time came for it to be put to the test Scott ordered everybody out of the building and knocked away the last support with his own hand. His work, for all that had gone into the dome was his, held. Many other experts had looked forward to something more dramatic. Despite all that Sir Henry Wood's promenaders, innumerable *Jerusalems'* and *'Hiawathas'* and the attentions of the Luftwaffe, would do, Scott's dome remains at the time of writing apparently as good as it was in 1870. Its creator had many subsequent achievements to his credit before dying as a Major-General in 1883. The Czar gave him a snuff-box set with diamonds, the Society of Arts presented him with a silver medal in recognition of his paper on 'Suggestions for dealing with the Sewerage of London' and similar honours were showered on him by International Exhibitions everywhere. He also found time to beget fifteen children. For all these experiences, however, one may fairly regard the apogee of Major-General Scott's life as being reached when he dauntlessly knocked out that last support.

On the matter of the photographs of South Kensington

Museum during the building, it seems pertinent to tell of the strong connections of the Royal Engineers with the development of that art. From its earliest beginnings it was obvious that the camera deserved a place at any rate on the outskirts of the battlefield. Many a regimental Mess has, or had until recently, framed examples of the work of Roger Fenton, taken in the Crimea, or those of Signor Beato recording for all time some horrors of the Indian Mutiny. Close behind them followed Matthew Brady, who had learned his trade from Samuel Morse and who followed the battles of the American Civil War with the dark room on wheels inside which he was reputed to live. So excellent were the products of all of them that to modern eyes they look unreal; more like stage sets, or stills from *Gone With The Wind,* than true likenesses of men at war. And yet they were the truest and most permanent likenesses ever made.*

The result of all this was that in 1874 Pasley's School of Military Engineering decided that the time had come for a full-blown department of photography to be added. There was only one candidate for its headship, but he was a man probably better fitted for the appointment than any other then living. William de Wive-Leslie Abney was the son of a Prebendary of Lichfield; his mother was a Strutt of Belper, whose family was ennobled in 1856, eight years after the birth of William. Her son, after Rossall, was sent to The Shop from where he was duly gazetted to the Royal Engineers in 1861. He was packed off almost at once to the Bombay Sappers and Miners for service in post-Mutiny India. He returned to England in 1867 and in 1871 was posted to Chatham as an assistant instructor in telegraphy. This lasted only a few months. Later in the year he became Instructor in Chemistry and Photography. Though hard evidence is lacking it seems highly probable that one of his students, reckoned at the time 'below rather than above the average standard of an RE officer', was Gentleman Cadet (after April, 1871 Second Lieutenant) Herbert Horatio Kitchener. There seems no other source of the instruction which enabled this young officer only four years later

* From its beginnings the practical uses of photography had interested the Corps. Sir Henry James in 1859 substituted photographic carbon prints for tracings and had them transferred to zinc for use by the Ordnance Survey.

to produce and cause to be published *Lieutenant Kitchener's Guinea Book of Photographs of Biblical Sites*. It was good value. One copy remains in the Corps Library.

In 1874 the department was elevated to a school in its own right. Abney, fascinated by the subject but necessarily self-taught, set himself to bring the advantages of a scientific mind to something that had so far been empirical. At the time the most advanced process was the wet collodion plate. A mixture of chemicals was poured on to glass, the plate was sensitised in a mixture of silver nitrate and water and put into the camera wet. As soon as the exposure had been made the plate, often large, was rushed into the dark room. Captain Abney, along with Mr Bennett and a Belgian chemist named van Monckhoven all made substantial contributions to the discovery of the rapid gelatine emulsion which made instant photography possible. Abney alone went on to examine further the whole chemistry of the business. In 1881 he introduced the gelatine-citro-chloride emulsion printing process, from which came the modern printing-out paper and he also wrote a rather famous book. Abney on *Photography With Emulsions* was the definitive work for many years. From there he moved on to cognate matters intelligible only to another chemist and finally to the matter of colour photography. By 1880 he had made photographic plates sensitive to the red and the infra-red with which he mapped this region of the solar spectrum. Of his many publications the last was *The Trichromatic Theory of Colour,* published in 1914.

No doubt if Captain Sir William Abney had never been born, or had been sent into a line regiment, somebody else would have invented these things; but they did not and his Corps can fairly assert that, in addition to all other entries in their cellarbook, they have a large share in the beginnings of the motion-picture industry and the humbler forms of photography.

IX

Opusculum: The Grand Shaft

BEFORE ENDING THIS CHRONICLE it seems worth while to tell of a piece of Sapper work very different from those already described; the difference is that between a mural and a miniature. Compared with By's and Cotton's people its makers stand as does Fabergé to Telford. To find it — and it takes some finding — you must travel to Dover, preferably before the whole of it collapses into the Channel Tunnel.

Even to those who love the place — and such there are — Dover nowadays is an unalluring little town mitigated by a number of peerless mediaeval buildings that stand out like gold nuggets in a prospector's pan. For two millennia it has been both port and garrison town where for centuries the trumpets of Imperial Rome greeted every dawn and sunset. Underneath some 15 acres of unattractiveness lie the richest treasures of Roman archaeology to be found anywhere in Britain; possibly anywhere outside Rome itself. Over the last few years it has been dug and wonderful things have appeared — parts of a great naval base, complete with barracks, granaries, walls, gatehouses and roads; of slightly more recent date was the Roman Army barracks, probably far bigger than any put up for the soldiers of all the Hanoverian kings and queens. For as near to four hundred years as makes no difference the Legions lived in Dover and marched through the town on their way to and from the camps to the north and west and even to the wall itself, Rome's own north-west frontier. The names IInd Augusta, IXth Hispana and XXth Valeria Victrix were as familiar to the burgesses and the publicans as, say, the Highland Light Infantry to our own generation, and for a great deal longer.*

---

* Only The Buffs, raised in 1572, have as long a continuous history.

What tangible relics they left behind them nobody yet knows in full, but the spades are becoming busy and they may unearth surprising things. The excellence of Roman military engineering is well known, for climates superior to ours have preserved more than we. Dover, when uncovered, may add much to our fund of knowledge. It is of some comfort to know that the skills of our Roman ancestors are still carried on by Pasley's successors not very many miles away.

The centuries pass (perhaps an historic present may be allowed just this once) and another kind of emperor appeared opposite, pitching his tent on the heights above Boulogne. It was not by accident that Bonaparte's Tour d'Odre neighboured Caligula's Tower. Not quite forty centuries looked down, across the sea at the cleft in the hills where Dover stands, but certainly half that number might be claimed. From both Eastern and Western Heights men and women could plainly see the lights of both Left Camp and Right Camp as the Grande Armée settled down for the evening meditating another Enterprise of England. Most to be feared were the moonlit nights with a small east wind and high tide about dawn. Then, and not for the first time by a long way, the unspoken question, 'Will they come today?' hung over the town. On this occasion it would be for Lord Nelson and the Royal Navy to give the answer. 'Not today. Nor for many days to come. Perhaps some other time.'

Long before Trafalgar, however, the Government had given a lot of thought to coastal defence and had taken the best advice that the Sappers could give. On the easternmost side of Dover town stood the castle, high on its cliff and looking as inexpugnable as it would in those later days when the vapour trails of Hurricane and Messerschmitt veiled it. On the Western Heights, however, was nothing much beyond some relics of Henry VIII's day. As this would never do, the Royal Staff Corps, who were building the Royal Military Canal, was pressed into service to furnish it with works equally defensible. The great engineer names of the period when Bonaparte threatened invasion are three, Moncrieff, Sutherland and Twiss; all are commemorated by the names of streets or buildings in their old headquarter town of Hythe. Each had his work to do, but the most important of the triumvirate was the last named.

William Twiss, whose parents economised on Christian names as did those of John By, was born in Yorkshire at about the moment when the Young Pretender was landing in Scotland. By the time the infants Arthur Wellesley and Napoleon Bonaparte (and, incidentally, Ludwig van Beethoven) first saw the light of day in 1769 Practitioner-Engineer-and-Ensign Twiss already had nearly seven years' service behind him. In 1776 he accompanied 'Gentleman Johnny' Burgoyne to America and saw some hard service before being among those captured at Saratoga. In particular he had worked under Sir Guy Carleton on the Saint Lawrence River at the hideously difficult business of building some sort of a fleet and putting it to work on Lake Champlain. The vessels sent from England all had to be taken to pieces and manhandled along with some big flatboats and 400 bateaux overland and against the powerful currents of the St John and St Thérèse rivers. The job was somehow done, and done well. After Saratoga, Twiss was exchanged and went back to Canada as Chief Engineer at the age of 32. His second tour was employed, among other things, in designing and having made new models of the Army's pick and shovel. It was a task giving little scope for ingenuity. After two centuries they still look familiar. In 1783 he returned home and after various postings of no particular interest he became, in 1795, Lieutenant-Governor of the Royal Military Academy, Woolwich. It seems a reasonable conjecture, though quite without evidence, that Brigadier-General Twiss there encountered Gentleman Cadet John By and may have interested him in the challenge of Canada.

The Shop was not his only responsibility. During his time there Twiss was put in overall charge of the coastal defences of Kent but they were not yet as critical as they were shortly to become. Twiss had plenty of leisure. When, in 1789, the Government invited him to examine the possibilities of a tunnel under the Thames at Gravesend he readily accepted. Indeed the scheme pleased him so much that when a joint-stock company was floated to carry out the work Twiss's name appeared amongst the directors. There was no urgency about it and a shaft was sunk during the year 1801. It cost far more than anybody had bargained for and the venture had to be abandoned. For Brigadier-General Twiss the loss was not total. He had learned much about the drilling of shafts and knowledge so valuable is never wasted. When he was ordered to draw up a comprehensive scheme for the fortification of the undefended parts of Dover it came in very useful indeed.

The Western Heights rise fairly sharply from a little way behind the beach. On the crest was built the barracks justly called the Citadel and, on a shelf a short distance below and to one side, sprang up another. The Citadel is now a Borstal Institution. The Grand Shaft Barracks, inhabited until well after Hitler's War, have been pulled down. The buildings have almost all gone but several acres of secondary jungle studded with pieces of abandoned roadways remain; solidly built flights of steps lead from nowhere to nowhere. Walk down one or other of them, through clinging and usually wet undergrowth, and you will come across a cup-shaped depression with a high circular fence around the middle of it. This is General Twiss's chef-d'oeuvre, the Grand Shaft.

The barracks contained something like a full battalion of infantry, serving as a kind of inlying piquet on the grand scale. Should the French land on Dover beach the battalion would instantly fall on them. That it would do almost literally unless some provision were to be made for orderly egress to a forming-up place below. The barracks, at its nearest point, was only about 300 yards from the beach; it was also 180 feet above it. Twiss reported in April, 1804, that 'The footpaths are so steep and chalky that a number of accidents will unavoidably happen during the wet weather and especially after floods'. This was, if anything, meiosis. The white cliffs are almost pure chalk and have a long history of releasing vast quantities to crash on to the town below. The Committee of Engineer Officers, led by a General d'Aubant, advised the building of a road. This, Twiss could plainly see, would never do; 'road' in 1804 did not mean a tarmac surface. In any event, he had a better idea. Most probably he had inherited it from a predecessor, but there is nothing wrong in that. During the American War, in 1779, there had been a French invasion scare at least as serious as that of 1804. A sapper officer of the time, Captain Hyde Page, had thought out the plan of 'A vertical shaft near the cliff edge with a triple staircase within it'. That the underlying idea is not new can be found by a tour of the

Loire chateaux. Chambord has its great circular stairway where it is claimed that persons beginning the ascent cannot meet those coming down at the same time. Something similar is built into the outside wall of Blois; at Amboise, in the Tour des Minimes, is a helical ramp built of brick winding gently around a central core and broad enough for artillery and wagons. Leonardo himself is reputed to have had a hand in some, at least, of these ingenuities. With such precedents and with such footsteps in which to tread it can hardly be surprising that William Twiss had confidence in his plan. The summer of 1804, like the summer of 1940, was not a time for debates; Twiss was a man in whom a Government could have confidence and he was ordered to get on with the work.

It began in the autumn of the same year. The plan was for a vertical shaft with a diameter of 26 feet and a depth of 140: inside it was to run a much smaller brick-built one, open at the top and pierced for windows throughout its depth. Between the two there would be a system of three helical staircases, one above the other and built from Purbeck stone brought by lighter. At the bottom the staircases would converge in a sloping corridor which opened on to the street. The object of it all, as Twiss wrote to his chief, General Morse, was 'to open the shortest and securest communication with the town and, at need, it would be useful for sending reinforcements to troops employed in the defence of the Beach and Town, or in affording them a safe retreat'.

Building the Shaft was a nightmare. Such a combination of chalk and water was not to be met by the Army again until the Somme: the weather over a long period was uniformly vile and at one point, in November, 1806, Twiss received a report from Captain Ford, the RE officer in charge, that was worrying. 'The Great Shaft has become so dangerous that I forbid all working there till 24 hours after the rain ceases; we have as yet had but one accident by the fall of a piece about a ton's weight which broke the stages all to atoms and carried one man to the bottom; he be very much bruised but (miraculously) doing well; we have got about 25 feet of the Steering up and 20 feet more will I think make us quite secure.' Ford had spoken too soon. A fortnight later 'So large a quantity of earth fell in last night that the scaffolding is entirely demolished and I really think it is not safe to risk the lives of men in attempting to re-establish it . . . it appears almost miraculous to me that every great fall has happened when the men were not at work'.

A year after the digging began the Royal Navy had seen off any real invasion threat and the Grande Armée acquired other interests. The urgency went out of making Dover defensible, but the work went on; probably more slowly, for it was 1809 when it was formally handed over for use. By then the Duke had set to work in Spain and the Shaft would be a convenience rather than a necessity. It had a handsome archway and sentrybox at its foot, from time to time somebody, on the 'because it was there' principle, rode a horse up it and the guard-room of Grand Shaft Barracks welcomed out-of-breath arrivals at the top. Though no longer of the slightest military importance, the Shaft remained a piece of masterly work. The historian W. H. Ireland, writing in the 1820s, treated of it with admiration. 'An ascent has been made from the town to the Heights, by means of a spiral staircase of stone, carried up a large shaft bored through the solid rock, and lighted by openings into the centre or area around which the steps are disposed. The entrance to this ingenious work is through an arched passage conducting from the level of the street, by a very gentle ascent, to the foot of the steps; when the latter, being divided into two branches, afford facility of access to many persons at the same time, both in mounting and descending. The landing-places, as well as the apertures for the admission of light, being properly secured by iron rails and gratings, accidents never occur; indeed, both the design and execution of this work are deserving the highest commendation. Such a union of elegance and convenience might have reflected credit even upon Sir Christopher Wren; at once combining the gracefulness of that stupendous vestige of architectural skill, the Monument of London, with the greatest simplicity and general accommodation.' For such a tribute Mr Ireland may be forgiven the slip of crediting the Shaft with two staircases only. His praise is deserved.

The little work now stands forlornly in the middle of weeds and brambles. For a long period it has fallen upon hard times. Once the barracks had gone and the place was deserted Young England did its customary best to foul everything and to use the Shaft as a rubbish tip. One expert managed to inveigle a wrecked motor car into the light well. Nobody manifested much interest. The future begins to look more encouraging. The local authority, to whom the Shaft now belongs, is making a brave effort at putting it back into its original condition and, with ordinary good fortune, this will soon be done. It will still be necessary to keep a strong padlock on the gates and to open it to the public only on Red Letter Days. 'Heritage' is a word that makes the heart sink, but it is better than death from neglect.

The journey is well worth while. Stand by the top of the Shaft, look out above the Hoverport over the Channel and shut your eyes; there is no knowing what ancient echoes from swearing red-coats may not come up to you. Then corkscrew your way to the bottom and up again. Though the Shaft was made to serve the purpose of a fire-station pole writ large, it manifests the kind of beauty that our ancestors were able, probably unconsciously, to build into everything they touched. The brick and stone work are the perfection of the bricklayers' and masons' arts; the very iron railings are of the same quality and the skill of the draughtsmen who made it all possible speak for themselves. Though oceans apart from the Rideau Canal, the Godavari anicuts and the Nile Barrage this little example of sapper workmanship on our own doorstep deserves its place in the archives. Excellence, no less than ubiquity, has always been the Corps' trade-mark.

X

The Royal Engineers and the Channel Tunnel

THE RAILWAY LINE between Folkestone and Dover, laid out in the late 1830s, runs along the foot of steep acclivities and within biscuit toss of the sea. Nearer to Dover it passes through a tunnel at the foot of Shakespeare's Cliff. In the first day or two of September, 1939, the present writer was ordered to take his company of Territorial infantry and set a guard over the place; it was never explained to him what he was guarding but the general understanding was that the tunnel contained much of the Navy's reserves of ammunition. Posts were immediately set up at either end, on top and around; most of them were accessible only by rail or on foot. A reconnaissance as thorough as time permitted was carried out and revealed interesting features. For example, there were ventilation shafts running up almost alongside a main road which beckoned to even the apprentice saboteur. More to the point was a discovery made near to the tent at the western end (properly called Abbot's Cliff) which housed a section. The corporal in command had turned up things even more interesting and he invited inspection. On opening a door in the earth a ramp was revealed, running out under the sea for — as near as we could guess — half a mile. At the end was a brick wall. Everything was in excellent order. On enquiring of the railway authorities what it was that we had found, the answer was clear. These were the old tunnel workings of Colonel Beaumont, carried out in 1882. Behind the wall, immured until the Last Trump should sound, was his compressed air drilling machine, the very last word in Victorian engineering technology. It would have to stay there until then because the money ran out long ago and nobody would ever bother with it again. Presumably it still lies there, waiting.

Colonel Beaumont was undoubtedly a man of parts, but the measure of credit, if that be the right word, given to him for the work is excessive. His share was that of the entrepreneur, the beater of the drum and the dispenser of good sherry to the influential. It is true that he invented a boring machine; equally true is it that the thing did not work. Beaumont's borer was sound in concept in that it was driven by compressed air,* but all it could do was empower percussive drills on a fixed head to cut a series of concentric circular grooves; these weakened the rock face which was then set about by navvies. It was hardly the way to dig a tunnel 20-odd miles under the sea. All the same, there was a way and a brother-Sapper invented it.

Thomas English was a man who compels admiration, not only for his superior professional skill but also for his uprightness of character. He had been gazetted to the Corps in December, 1862, and his first posting of any moment might be envied even now. He was sent with a party of sappers to the island of Corfu with orders to blow up the old British fortifications there and on Vido island. That done, he interested himself above all things in a matter much debated at the time, the conflict between shell and armour; his writings on the subject in the 1870s seem to have been overlooked when the first tanks were built. They could have saved much grief. English had his quota of the strange demands made upon Victorian sappers. They are recorded in his own book, privately published and of which the only known surviving copy is in the library at Chatham. For example, he has a fine photograph of his people hoisting an 80-ton muzzle-loading gun on to Dover Pier using sheer legs and muscle power. Its purpose was to enfilade the Channel Tunnel works if needed.† By much the same means, in May, 1882, he obliged the Dean and Chapter of St Paul's by heaving a 17-ton bell to its place in the south-west tower. His claim to fame, however, was in mastering the uses of compressed air. It was a fashionable subject in the late '70s, with several metropolitan railways working quite efficiently under its

* Compressed air machinery had been used for drilling the Mont Cenis tunnel in the 1860s.
† The gun, a rifled 13'5" bottle-shaped monster, remains with its twin, bricked up in the same turret. The elaborate steam engines for loading, traversing and elevating have long gone. Apparently what is left does not warrant the cost of removal.

power.* For some reason they did not endure: probably because air escaped too easily through unsophisticated piping.

English came into contact with Beaumont during the summer of 1879 and eventually they went into partnership. His diary entries for the period are set out below. In the face of their evidence it is hard to support the proposition that a jealous subordinate later set out to discredit his senior.

1879:

July 21st. I discussed with Colonel Beaumont, RE, MP, the possibility of using a tunnel driving machine for boring the proposed trial heading for the Channel Tunnel between Dover and Calais.

July 22nd. Visited a tunnel for the Great Northern Railway at Keighley, in Yorkshire, where Colonel Beaumont is driving a heading with rock-drills and dynamite.

August 17th. With Colonel Beaumont visited the boring at Sangatte, which is being sunk by the French Engineers, below the sea-level, to explore for a suitable stratum in which to locate the French end of the tunnel.

September 23rd. Went with Colonel Beaumont to Halkyn Deep Level, North Wales, where he is engaged on a contract for unwatering the neighbouring groups of mines, and is working with rock-drills and dynamite.

October 22nd. Met Sir E. Watkin, M.P., Chairman of the South Eastern Railway Co., and Colonel Beaumont, at Dover.

October 23rd. Walked over the ground between Dover and Folkestone with Colonel Beaumont, and discussed with Sir E. Watkin terms for driving an experimental heading descending about 1/80 from some point which we are to fix. He would pay £3 per yard.

October 25th. Walked over the ground again, found that

---

* Major-General Sir Charles Callwell tells in his Memoirs of a huge gun worked by compressed air and firing a dynamite-filled shell being set up near the port of Milford Haven. 'The puff of air not being sufficient to give the shell a real good biff to make it travel the gun was not supposed to be an accurate piece of ordnance even for the very short ranges up to which it could fire.' This was flattering; the thing proved quite useless. *Stray Recollections*, Arnold, 1923, vol. 2, P.10.

there was no apparent fault at Lydden Spout, but a synclinal dip in the chalk, beneath which the heading might safely pass.

October 26th. Wrote to Colonel Beaumont as follows: — "I got yours this morning, and have been most of the day about it. I thought it so important to determine what the water at Lydden Spout comes from, that yesterday I took Lieut. Lewis, RE, a very good geologist and a sharp fellow, and had a thorough examination, coming to the conclusion that there is certainly no fault there, but that the spring is due to clayey beds throwing off the water at that point owing to a slight reversed dip. The normal dip from Folkestone to the Spout is 1/110, for 200 yards beyond the spout the beds rise 1/50 towards Dover. I think that this throws out the water from a long stretch towards Folkestone, which would otherwise drain along their surface. These beds reach high water mark about the west end of Shakespeare's Cliff Tunnel. Several things confirm this —

(1) Lydden Spout comes out about 15 feet above H.W.M.

(2) and we found almost exactly the same thing on a smaller scale about two hundred and fifty yards west, where were the same beds, throwing out a small weep owing to a slight reversed dip.

(3) In the French Chart some clayey beds are marked, throwing out springs at Blanc Nez *(Sources du Creu d'Escalles)*.

(4) In the boring at Sangatte, the least water (0.15 litres per minute) per metre run of depth, was found beneath these springs, which are on the same horizon as Lydden Spout.

Also I was satisfied that the sandy clay, just above the gault, which represents the upper Greensand, and gradually shades off into clayey beds of the Lower Chalk, will not let water pass. I took samples of the most sandy bits, and saw plenty of clay in them.

I think that the beds above Lydden Spout are dry in the cliff, only because they allow water to pass downwards, and that below the sea level they will be quite waterlogged.

Therefore, I think that the present heading should be made in the best bed we can find between Lydden Spout and the Gault, giving 90-100 feet for choice, and that the tunnel should follow the same strata across ...."
Yours,
THO. ENGLISH.

Copy of letter from Colonel Beaumont and Captain English to Sir E. Watkin.
Westminster Palace Hotel,
29th October, 1879
Dear Sir Edward,

With reference to our recent conversation on the subject of the Channel Tunnel, and the commencement of a trial heading from a point on the South Eastern Railway between Dover and Folkestone, we now have pleasure in submitting the following offer:—

We will drive a heading not less than seven feet in the clear for the sum of £3 per yard lineal forward.

We will find all labour, boring machinery, air compressors, receivers and pipes for the same, and all other tackle necessary for properly carrying on the work, excepting the following which would be provided by you:—

Any timber or lining, should such be required, you to give us the use of a boiler to supply our engine with steam, water and fuel for the same, the use of rails and sleepers, and the carriage of men and materials, free of cost as far as the South Eastern Railway is concerned.

You to execute any pumping which may be required, and provide the requisite machinery and pipes.

We have carefully examined the ground, and selected the point marked A on the accompanying plan as the most suitable one to commence at.

It is in the gray chalk, about sixty feet above the gault, and is situated in a secluded gulley offering ample room for the erection of the machinery and disposal of the debris, and ready communication with your line.

The heading will commence by a level drift passing under your line, about 25 feet below it, and continuing until the solid strata are reached, when the tunnel will turn to the right, and drop, at an inclination of 1/80 along the line which we would recommend for the permanent tunnel.

The sea level will be reached in about one mile, exclusive of the level drift, and the level of sixty feet below the sea would be reached after about two miles of driving, and at a cost, irrespective of the plant provided by you, of some £10,500.

Much of the doubt attaching to the undertaking would then have been solved, as the first sixty feet below the sea level constitutes, in all probabililty, the most risky part of the undertaking.

As regards speed of driving, our machinery is capable of completing the heading across the Channel in two years after the commencement from both sides, assuming no interrupting by water.

We trust you will see your way to commence the work at once, in the way proposed.

There is, of course, no absolute certainty of success, at the same time it appears to us in the highest degree probable that no serious amount of water will be met with, so long as the heading is kept low down in the grey chalk.

Fissures are most to be dreaded, but an inspection of the nature of the material will show how little likely it is that any fissures, should they exist, will be open for any considerable distances.

It is, however, absolutely impossible to prove this point without the trial which, we trust, will now be made. We would suggest that the terms of the proposed agreement should be binding on either side, for the first mile of mechanical driving only.
We are, Dear Sir Edward,
Yours faithfully,
(Sd.) F. BEAUMONT.
T. ENGLISH.
Sir E. Watkin, Bart,. M.P.,
Chairman, S.E. Railway.

The stratum which I recommended, for geological

reasons, to be used for the experimental heading on the English side having been agreed to, the provision of a boring machine capable of driving the heading in the shortest possible time, became a necessity, and in December 1879, I completed a detailed design for the adaptation of Colonel Beaumont's original tunnelling machine, which was then at Messrs. John Fowler & Co.'s Works at Leeds, to meet the requirements temporarily, and furnish the information necessary before constructing an entirely new machine.

The original machine was intended to produce a circular heading, seven feet in diameter, by the use of compressed air, and percussive drills so arranged as to cut concentric circular grooves in the face of the heading, thus weakening the rock sufficiently to allow of its being wedged off and removed by hand, after the grooves had been completed, when the machine would be free to travel forward on small trucks bearing on the lower portion of the completed heading.

It had been found, however, in practice, that it was difficult to ensure sufficient fixing for the carrying trucks, and the main alteration consisted in substituting for them, longitudinal metallic sliding surfaces between the frame of the cutting machinery and a wrought iron foundation similar to a lathe bed, of which the underside was cylindrical so as to lie in contact, all over, with the lower surface of the heading already cut.

It was arranged that the whole machine, including this bed, could be raised by jacks on the completion of a cut, and that the bed could then be traversed forward underneath the machine by an auxiliary compressed-air engine, so that when the machine was lowered again by the jacks, it would be in position for commencing another cut.

I also considered it desirable to abandon the use of percussive drills, and to provide for cutting away the whole face of the heading into chips, by means of a rotating boring head, the full diameter of the heading, furnished with removable cutting chisels which could be taken out and sharpened, and driven by a double cylinder compressed-air engine mounted on the upper sliding frame.

It was also necessary to provide for the continued removal of the chips, through the machine to the back, where they could be emptied into trollies on a portable railway, laid up to the machine.

On the 3rd March, 1880, Colonel Beaumont and I met Sir E. Watkin, Mr Fenton, the General Manager, and Mr Brady, the Engineer of the South Eastern Railway Co; and finally arranged that the trial heading on our proposed line and level, should start from the bottom of a shaft to be sunk, nearly to high water mark, from the level of the S.E. Railway, in order to test the conditions under the sea level as early as possible, before driving the portion of the heading necessary for connection with the S.E. Railway, and that Colonel Beaumont and I should select the actual site for the shaft.

March 4th, 1880. We sent the following memorandum:-
"After careful consideration we suggest the shaft being commenced as close to the railway as possible, in the hollow on the sea side immediately adjoining the Folkestone end of the Abbot's Cliff Tunnel. It should be sunk to high water mark, when it will be as near to the Upper Greensand as it is prudent to go, say 15 to 20 feet above it. The heading should then be driven at an inclination of 1/80 in a straight line towards Dover. We would suggest 12 feet by 6 feet as a convenient size for the shaft. After the drift way has been satisfactorily commenced a short heading may be driven in an opposite direction, coming out today above the sea level so as to save lifting the debris up the shaft."

(Sd.) F. BEAUMONT.
THO. ENGLISH

Sir E. Watkin gave instructions for the work to proceed, and also asked me to prepare a design for a more powerful new machine, embodying whatever improvements we might find desirable from the experience gained with the altered one in this heading, in order to commence the actual submarine tunnel headings as early as possible.

The shaft, and a level heading between it and the beach, were completed by the 6th July, 1880, and at the same date the altered boring machine was tested, under steam, at Messrs. John Fowler & Co.'s Works at Leeds.

On July 20th, 1880, Mons. Leon Say and the French Engineers visited Abbot's Cliff and expressed their satisfaction with the arrangements.

It appeared that the positions, geologically, of the proposed headings at Abbot's Cliff and Sangatte, which had been selected entirely independently, and without knowledge, in either case, of what had been done on the other side, corresponded very closely to the same horizon, allowing for the differences in the thicknesses of the beds.

The Abbot's Cliff heading is about 30 metres below the horizon of Lydden Spout, whilst the thickness of the beds found to be impervious, above the heading floor and below the horizon of the Sources du Creu d'Escalles at Sangatte is 29 metres.

On 31st July, 1880, the boring machine arrived at Folkestone, and on the 10th September the erection of the machine commenced, in the chamber prepared for it, for cutting towards Dover, parallel to the S.E. Railway and with the centre line 30 feet inland from the down rail.

On the 18th September, 1880, Mons. Breton, the Engineer to the French Compagnie du Chemin de Fer Sousmarin, called and had the arrangements explained to him. He said they were waiting to see how we got on, and had decided nothing.

On 16th October, 1880, the machine started cutting the full face of the heading, and on the 25th October, I applied for Letters Patent for it, No. 4347—1880.

On 13th November Sir E. Watkin, Messrs. Fenton and Brady visited the works. Sir E. Watkin said that he would recommend Baron Rothschild to come to Colonel Beaumont and myself for the French side.

On 4th January, 1881, all machine adjustments and minor alterations were completed, and everything is now satisfactory and workable.

On 29th January, 1881, Sir E. Watkin gave orders for a shaft to be sunk between Abbot's Cliff and Dover to commence fresh headings from. Mr Brady and I to select the site.

On 1st February, 1881, with Mr Brady, marked out the site for a shaft, 75 feet south of the nearest rail, near the west end of Shakespeare's Cliff Tunnel, to be put in hand at once, with a siding.

February 5th and March 26th, 1881, Mons. Breton and other French Engineers visited the works.

April 22nd, 1881, Sir E. Watkins, Mons. Leon Say, Mons. Raoul Duval, Mons. Le Valley, and the Directors of the South Eastern Railway inspected the works.

May 14th. Inspection by Board of Trade.

May 20th, 1881. Received a letter from Mons. Raoul Duval asking Colonel Beaumont and myself to go to Paris with reference to a contract for the French side.

May 26th, 1881. Ordered the new machine from Messrs. J. Fowler & Co., Leeds.

May 28th, 1881. Arranged with Sir E. Watkin and Mr Fenton that the present heading is to be continued to half a mile, after which the present machine is to drive not less than half a mile at Shakespeare's Cliff.

June 9th, 1881. Met Messrs. Fenton and Brady, who now propose that the South Eastern Railway Co. should carry on the work at Shakespeare's Cliff, hiring the machinery from Colonel Beaumont and myself.

June 14th, 1881. Agreed with M. Raoul Duval to commence work at Sangatte, and ordered a machine from Gouin & Co., Paris, for a heading 7 feet 2 inches diameter, to the same drawings as the one which Fowler & Co. have in hand.

July 21st, 1881. Completed 880 yards at Abbot's Cliff, the last yard being a speed and endurance test for the machine, with 7/12 of an inch feed against the face per revolution, 40 lbs. per inch air pressure at the compressors, and a heavy blow-off at the machine, with safety valve set at 22 lbs. per inch. The machine made 41 revolutions in 47 minutes, cutting 24 inches, everything stood and the chips were 12 inches long, but the machine was very unsteady, nearly twisting over.

August 13th, 1881. Everything is now removed to Shakespeare's Cliff.

August 31st, 1881. Refitting at Shakespeare's Cliff with new bucket — and endless chain-gear passing through the machine, for removing debris.

As soon as the two above-mentioned new machines, ordered from Messrs. Fowler's and Gouin's were completed, they were set to work at Shakespeare's Cliff and Sangatte respectively, each obtaining a speed of advance of 27 yards in 24 hours.

When about 2,950 yards had been bored in the two headings at Dover, and 1,829 yards at Sangatte, without difficulty or mishap, the work on the English side was stopped, by order of the Board of Trade, in 1882.

There was no object in continuing the heading on the French side, and nothing further has since been done towards the construction of the tunnel.

A silver medal was awarded, 28th October, 1885: "To Major English and Colonel Beaumont for a Boring Machine," by the Jury Commission of the International Inventions Exhibition, London.

The new machine made by Fowler & Co. was sold, as it stood in the heading, in September, 1887, to the Channel Tunnel Company, and the machine made by Gouin & Co. was removed from the heading at Sangatte, and sold to Messrs. Bewick and Moreing, Mining Engineers.

In the *Illustrated London News* for 4 March, 1882, is an article over the signature 'James Seymour' of whom nobody knows anything. He tells posterity that 'most categorically they (the tunnelling machines) are not the development of Colonel Beaumont but of Captain (sic) English, and as such patented by him two years ago. English does not wish to debase the efforts or achievements of Colonel Beaumont but if pressed will talk of the improvements manifest in 'his' machine'. The Submarine Continental Railway Company, almost wholly owned by the Southern Railway, kept up a steady flow of visitors and the Lord Warden Hotel thrived. The machine was driven by air forced through 4-inch iron pipes from a compressor at the shaft mouth; this also provided ventilation. When finished, the tunnel would become a highway for Beaumont's compressed air locomotives, travelling at 30 mph. Seymour warmed to his subject. 'The Channel Tunnel locomotive will weigh from 60 to 70 tons and will be charged with 1200 cubic feet of air, compressed to the density of 70 atmospheres, the equivalent of which is over 80,000 cubic feet of free air. This will give power sufficient to draw a train of 150 tons gross weight (including the engine) the distance of 22 miles under the sea . . . the air discharged by the engine would give a supply of free and pure air to the amount of 2,000 cubic feet, approximately, which will be far in excess of what is needed by the passengers in the train.' All this would have been due to English and, from a professional point of view, it is a pity that the money ran out and work stopped.

It has been said that English deserves praise for officer-like behaviour. 'Captain English is both modest and a gentleman, one who is not inclined to claim credit for events, even when it is obviously due but so cruelly withheld. His position as employee to Sir Edward and as junior colleague of Colonel Beaumont makes discretion about the origin of the invention something of a necessity. Seeing numerous references to "Beaumont's tunnelling machine" or "the tunnelling machine of Beaumont and an unknown inventor" must be extremely galling, however, although English himself refuses to confirm this. "I cannot speak on the subject. It is neither fitting nor proper", he says'. Mr Seymour avers that relations between the two men were becoming 'increasingly strained', but he was getting nothing out of Major English, beyond 'I believe those in a position to judge such matters will come to know exactly what my contributions have been. It is my earnest hope that an honest account of my worth becomes available to all.' For all his dignified language English was as near to losing his temper as a man may come; his detestation of Beaumont was absolute. Though he had been less than fairly treated by his partner — English ought not to have trusted a regular officer turned MP so far — his life was not finished nor was it entirely unrewarding. Between 1903 and 1908 he, for his own amusement, made a detailed examination of the Gallipoli Peninsula and made copious notes illustrated by photographs of possible beachheads. Nobody else seems to have known. He was well enough off in 1914 to put his private yacht and crew at the disposal of the Admiralty, which gratefully accepted. All the same, Beaumont MP has all the fame; nobody has heard of English. Few Kentish hearts will break if history repeats itself and the money runs out again. But it does not seem likely that such good fortune can come a third time.

XI

Envoi from the Coast:
Sir Gordon Guggisberg

THIS BOOK BEGAN with a description of how The Shop came into being and something of how it carried out its mission. The greater part of this was extracted from a single source, *The Shop,* published in 1902 and written by Captain Frederick Gordon Guggisberg, RE, then aged 32. It seems only fair that, having had the first word, he should also have the last, for his name is among the great ones of the Corps.

Guggisberg has all the right credentials, for he was born in Canada and, apart from some heroic work between 1914 and '18, it was in the less manicured parts of the Empire that he made his name. He entered into the world in Toronto on 20 July, 1869, with a father of German-Swiss antecedents and an American mother. He was brought to England at the age of 10, educated at the famous Burney's school near Portsmouth and entered The Shop during the Jubilee year of 1887. He does not seem to have enjoyed himself immoderately as a 'snooker', but time cured all ills for him as it does for most people. It was ten years later, after a tour of Singapore, that he was brought back to Woolwich as an instructor (a notably reforming one) and wrote his book. His affection for the place shines plainly through it.

In 1902 he began his most enduring work, the surveys of the colonies and protectorates in West Africa. By then, four years after Omdurman, the 'scramble for Africa' was virtually over; the international task was to settle upon some sort of acceptable frontier line while internally the surveyors found out what sort of countries they had inherited and mapped them.

The British colonies, always collectively referred to as 'The

203

Coast', numbered four. The Gambia, Prince Rupert's old haunt, was probably the earliest acquisition, with Sierra Leone — a great gathering place for convoys since convoys were invented — close behind. Nigeria, much of it hardly explored, was by far the biggest; the Gold Coast, as its name suggests, had something denied to the others and was, for its size, the richest. Behind the Gold Coast Colony lay the Kingdom of Ashanti, tucked away inside its great rain forest, and beyond Ashanti lay the fairly open orchard bush of the slightly Moslem Northern Territories. It was from the tribes living here that the West African Frontier Force recruited its soldiers. Guggisberg was appointed first to perform a special survey of everything south of the Northern Territories, promoted to Director of Surveys in 1905 and kept at the task until 1908. It cannot have been the happiest of times, in the aftermath of the siege of Kumasi, but the survey was started and some work was done to move this part of Africa out of the early iron age. The first railway, linking the Obuasi goldfields with Kumasi and Sekondi, had been opened in 1904. Only gold can work such wonders. The roads were still much as Sir Garnet Wolseley had found them in 1874.

After a couple of years at Chatham, Guggisberg went back to the Coast in 1910, this time as Director of Surveys for Southern Nigeria. His work was reckoned by the Director-General to be a model of its kind. His handbook, written for the guidance of subordinates, laid down firmly that there must be no making the villagers work for nothing, that all goods should be paid for at market prices and care should be taken not to damage crops. The Director-General seemed to find this both praiseworthy and surprising, though no British officer would have even considered doing otherwise. When Northern Nigeria was united, at any rate on paper, with the south in 1913 Guggisberg was made Surveyor-General of the whole, an enormous task. For some lost reason he was, in 1914, transferred back to the Gold Coast as Director of Public Works. On this occasion he remained for an even shorter time. Every regular Sapper officer was desperately needed in France.

Guggisberg's part in the Great War was as distinguished as one might expect from someone of his quality. Until just before the Somme he commanded a Field Company; from that he was promoted to be CRE of the unluckiest Division on the Western Front, the 8th. He was in time for the disastrous attack at Gommecourt, after which he was posted to the newest Division to see service, the 66th. After a spell as CRE there, Guggisberg was elevated to the rank of Brigadier-General and given command of an infantry brigade. Even in 1918 such an appointment was not all that common among Sapper officers and it spoke for itself. He ended the war as Inspector of Training at GHQ.

Once the war was over Brigadier-General Guggisberg and his wife were fortunate enough to be returned to their beloved Gold Coast. Mrs Guggisberg, better known to theatre-goers by her stage name of Decima Moore, had accompanied him there on the earlier tour and, in 1909, she had been joint author of their book, *We Two In West Africa*. The Gold Coast Regiment, like those other parts of the WAFF, the Nigeria Regiment, the Sierra Leone Battalion and the Gambia Company, had made for itself a very high reputation during his absence both in East Africa and the Cameroons. The West African soldier is one of the most likeable men on earth, cheerful, loyal and enduring. In addition to these virtues he is endowed with a sense of fun which makes for easy and cordial relations with British officers and NCOs. Guggisberg understood and appreciated such qualities. One may fairly guess him to have regretted not being in either German East or the Cameroons where it was said by all hands that 'The Green Caps never go back.* Nonetheless, he set about the entirely congenial work of trying to make a better life for the returned soldier, along with his friends and relations. The old 'White Man's Grave' label was still firmly pinned upon anything to do with any part of West Africa and it was not entirely nonsense. The regular five grains of liquid quinine a day was quite essential as a prophylactic; even thus fortified the malaria still came. It took more than netting around the bed and long suede boots after dusk to outwit the anopheles mosquito. Nevertheless, it was a popular station, especially among penurious army officers. A tour of 18 months, officially reckoned as much as most Europeans could stand, gave the opportunity of enjoying life and saving a little money.

* Soldiers of the WAFF wore a small, round green headdress called, doubtless for good reason, a Kilmarnock cap.

For a start Guggisberg reactivated the Survey, something much needed before serious public works could be undertaken. The man to whom much of the field work was given was another Sapper whose name will not be forgotten in West Africa for a little while. Major Christopher Woolner, RE, had been through the war on the western front in much the same fashion as his chief and had been much decorated for gallantry. His task was the usual first priority, the making of decent maps of a country part rain forest and part savannah. There were still great tracts of it that no European had ever seen.

Then came the matter of roads. Since time began the country had managed well enough with bush paths, for the tsetse fly restricted the horse to certain corners of the Northern Territories only. Without horses there had been no demand for wheels; travellers walked from one place to another, often covering great distances. Important people, like chiefs, travelled in hammocks depending from a pole on the shoulders of two bearers. This was the customary vehicle for the European civilian, whose dignity did not permit him to move on his own feet. Until the coming of the motor lorry, roads, as the word is generally understood, did not exist. By the date of Guggisberg's governorship it was obvious that something had to be done about it.

For a start he set up a Provisional Roads Board, with all the powers needed to align and make something like a system. The Roman pattern was hardly appropriate in a country where rain comes down as it does not in Europe. It has been described as like being under a lake from which the bottom is suddenly removed, and inevitably no work can ever be regarded as finished. There was, however, one compensation. The soil, as red as Devonshire, yielded up great quantities of the ferruginous red clay called laterite which, after cooking in the sun for a while, produced a surface much like a hard tennis court. As no Sappers, other than the surveyors, were available the Governor did the next best thing. He called in the descendants of Rome, the Italian road-building contractors, who retained much of the old genius. Even after a couple of thousand years they were still the supreme practitioners, especially in Africa. The zig-zag road up the Aburi scarp, at the back of Accra, remains a testimonial to them. The roads and their accompanying bridges which traversed the Colony from the verge of the Sahara to the sea were soon carrying considerable numbers of the open-sided and over-crowded motor lorries locally called 'mammy trucks'. It made a great difference to life.

Two more things were needed for a land more or less fit for heroes to live in. The Gold Coast had neither an institution of higher education nor a harbour. Both were near to the heart of Sir Gordon, as he became in 1922, and he campaigned vigorously to wring money from a hard-up home Government. It was his pertinacity that made possible the establishment of the University College at Achimota and the provision of competent teachers. This gave him more pleasure than anything, for it was a matter about which he held decided views. Long experience of the King's African subjects had convinced him that their brains were in no way inferior to those of Europeans but were denied their chance of showing it for want of teaching. The proposition was not universally regarded as sound and Guggisberg had to overcome many difficulties before he had his plans accepted.

To set up Achimota College had been difficult enough. The creation of a regular port with proper harbour and railway installations fit to receive the biggest sea-going ships likely to be trading in those parts was harder still. For many generations the traditional way of arriving in Accra was to be lowered in a box over the ship's side and dropped into a heavily pitching surf-boat. The water shoals quickly from the beach, the surf boat did not get its name for nothing, and the passage could be a wet one. The paddlers managed admirably but the capacity of a boat that has, when emptied, to be rolled up the beach cannot be great. Though hardly high-technology the journey of a mile or more was exhilarating.*

Nothing could be made of Accra. Fortunately there lay well to the west another window on the sea at Takoradi, to which place both gold and cocoa were sent by rail. Here Guggisberg built his deep-water port, complete with moles, breakwater and all the paraphernalia that ports demand. There was no other of its kind on the entire bulge of West Africa and it did much to help in the

---

* The present writer, having thus arrived more than fifty years ago, remains persuaded that as the boat grounded somebody murmured 'Well rowed, Balliol'.

defeat of Rommel's Afrika Korps. It was at Guggisberg's Takoradi that the giant packing cases were unloaded and from them were taken the dismantled American aircraft to be flown to the Middle East. One may speculate what might have happened had Takoradi never been built; the answer contains little comfort.

Guggisberg left the Coast in 1928 and died two years later. His legacies of the visible and tangible kind were the roads, the University and the harbour. There was another, quite intangible. In 1943, when the war was going badly in the Far East, the Sapper Christopher Woolner, by than a Major-General, was ordered to form, from the units scattered about the four colonies, a division of all arms for operations against the Japanese. The African soldier's conditions of service did not oblige him to operate outside the African continent. Every man had to be invited to volunteer and it was a point of honour to make certain that no pressure was applied nor anyone misled. Very few hung back. It was Woolner's task to create a formation of a kind not seen before, based not on wheeled vehicles but on head carriers and trained to live and fight in those thick and mountainous parts of Burma coloured green on the map and labelled 'Dense mixed jungle, mainly bamboo; unsurveyed'. Battle drills unknown in Europe had to be worked out and new forms of training were invented; nearly all of them were Woolner's personal handiwork. Inevitably they did not all turn out as planned and had to be modified, but the idea was sound. Before long another West African division, the 82nd, trained and equipped for operations of a more conventional kind, was on its way. It is, perhaps, not too far fetched to think that the hand of Guggisberg, the best-loved Governor the Gold Coast ever had, was somewhere at work in such a display of imperial loyalty.

The old Accra cantonments are now called Burma Camp. They earned the name well.

NOTES ON SOURCES

I *The Opening of The Shop* (pp 8-14)

Almost everything to do with the Royal Military Academy, Woolwich comes from *The Shop* by Captain F. G. Guggisberg, Cassell, 1902.

II *Further Education* (pp 15-29)

In the Corps Library of the Royal Engineers are two copies of a very large book bearing the title *General Sir Charles Pasley, KCB, His Family and His Career.* Each copy is written entirely in manuscript and the accession plate bears the label 'Presented by Colonel John C. Tyler, JP, 2 Jan'y. '36'. One has to stand in awe at the industry which went into it.

The other sources are too obvious to need explanation.

III *Colonel By and the Defence of Canada* (pp 30-68)

Professional Papers of the Royal Engineers, 4th series, vols. 1, 2 and 5.

PRO WO44/32 pp 157-9.

PRO WO46/136 pp 58-64.

Papers of The Historical Society of Ottawa.

Parliamentary Papers on The Canadian Canals, 1832.

Rideau Waterway by Robert Legget, O.C., University of Toronto Press, 1972.

Colonel By's Friends Stood Up, Crocus House, Ottawa, 1979.

The Canadas by Sir Richard Bonnycastle, 1842.

Captain Marryat by D. Hannay, Walter Scott, 1889.

The Autobiography of Lieut.-General Sir Harry Smith Murray, 1902.

The work went on after the death of Colonel By. In the Borough Museum at Berwick-Upon-Tweed is a poster dated 30 March 1837, and headed *Emigration to British North America.* It announces that Messrs. J. & G. Carr were authorised 'to hire labourers for the Saint Lawrence Canal on *TERMS HIGHLY ADVANTAGEOUS'.* The place of assembly was nearby in Scotland, at Greenlaw.

The observations on mosquitoes and malaria are based upon an extensive acquaintance with both.

IV *Epilogue in Australia* (pp 69-77)

A History of The Colony of Victoria by H. G. Turner, Longmans, 1904.

The Cruise of HMS Galatea 1867-1868 by John Milner and O. W. Brierly, W. H. Allen, 1869.

They Built South Australia by D. A. Cumming and G. C. Moxham, 1986.

Australian Dictionary of National Biography, Vol. 2, Melbourne University Press, 1967.

V *General Cotton and the Irrigation of India* (pp 78-104)

As mentioned in the text, there is a biography of Sir Arthur Cotton, written by his daughter, Lady Hope, and published by Hodder & Stoughton in 1890. The other essential printed book is Vol. 2 of *The Military Engineer in India* by Lieut.-Col. Sandes, DSO, MC, RE; this is the locus classicus on the subject. In retirement Sir Arthur gave many lectures, the texts of some appearing in the biography, and I have drawn freely upon them. The Royal Engineers Journal for 1st September and 1st October, 1890, contain the 'Memorandum On The Engineering Works In The Madras Presidency of India Of Major-General Sir Arthur Cotton KCSI, RE'. Included is a copy of a letter from Miss Florence Nightingale in praise of his achievements.

I have been greatly helped by the generous advice given by Major-General Rau, AVSM and the late Chief Engineer (Irrigation) of Andhra Pradesh, Mr. K. V. Srinavasa Rao.

The India Office Library holds many more of the papers and pamphlets written by Sir Arthur than can be used in a book of this size.

VI *Paene Ubique* (pp 105-137)

Palmer's Report on his journey from North Bentinck Arm, published by the Royal Engineers press at New Westminster, is in the Corps Library at Chatham. On the shelves there are also several doctoral theses of relevance to this and cognate subjects. Palmer's Obituary is in the *RE Journal* for 1st May, 1893.

The printed books I have found the most useful (standard authorities apart) are these:

Sappers: The Royal Engineers in British Columbia. Beth Hill. Horsdal & Schubert, Ganges BC, 1987.

The Work of the Royal Engineers in British Columbia 1858-1863. His Honour Judge Frederic W. Howay, Victoria BC, 1910.

The Early History of the Fraser River Mines, by the same author.

The Diaries of Parker Pasha, edited by H. V. F. Winstone, Quartet Books, 1983.

Angela Burdett-Coutts and the Victorians by Clara Burdett Patterson, John Murray, 1953.

The Storming of the Taku Forts by H. H. Armstrong, 1896.

The Life of Sir Harry Parkes by S. Lane-Poole and F. V. Dickins, 1894.

Kipling's Japan by Cortazzi and Webb, Athlone Press 1988. Pamphlets, periodicals etc.

First Impressions: Letter of Colonel Richard Clement Moody, RE, to Arthur Blackwood, Feb. 1st 1859. Published, with much explanatory matter, by Willard E. Ireland in the *BC Historical Quarterly, 15,* 86-108, 1951.

VII *Egypt and the Sudan: Sir Colin Scott-Moncrieff* (pp 138-165)

There is an article on Egyptian irrigation in general terms by Colonel

Scott-Moncrieff in the *RE Journal,* Vol. 21, 1891. A Memoir by Sir Robert Hanbury Brown on the work done by Colonel Western is in Volume 25, 1917. His own memorial is in Vol. 40. Printed books include:

The British Expedition to Egypt, Sir Robert Wilson, W. Chalk, 1803.

The Land of the Nile: Egypt Past and Present, W. H. Davenport, Nelson 1872.

Eothen, A. W. Kinglake, Henry Frowde, 1906.

The War in Syria, Commodore Charles Napier, Parker, 1842.

The Rob Roy on the Jordan, John McGregor, John Murray, 1874.

Canals and Campaigns, Major-General Sir George Scott-Moncrieff, British Association for Cemeteries in SE Asia, 1897.

The Royal Engineers in Egypt, Lieut.-Col. E. W. C. Sandes, RE Institution, 1937.

The Life of Sir Colin Scott-Moncrieff, Mary Albright Hollings.

Thanks for the Memory, Mary Repington, Constable, 1938.

IX *Opusculum: The Grand Shaft* (pp 183-189)

Before any written sources I gratefully acknowledge the help of Mr. Mark Frost of Dover Museum.

The Grand Shaft by Sarah Campbell, *Bygone Kent,* Vol. 4, 1983.

The Western Heights Defences at Dover, David Burridge, *Bygone Kent,* Vol. 4, 1983.

History of Kent, W. H. Ireland, Vol. 2. Virtue, 1829.

PRO MS WO 55/778.

Personal knowledge.

XI *Envoi from the Coast* (pp 203-208)

Not a great deal of matter of record is uesful for learning about the work of Sir Gordon Guggisberg. The various numbers of *The Gold Coast Year Book,* published annually by the Colonial office have their uses. Guggisberg's own book, written jointly with A. G. Fraser and called *The Future of The Negro* was published in 1929, the year before his death, and treats of his views on African education. He found little upon which to congratulate the Colonial office. There is a letter, referred to in the *DNB,* written on his death-bed in which he tells of his love of Africa and its people. *The Royal Engineers Journal* for March, 1931, is his official memorial.

These things apart, I have been lucky enough to be able to draw more than usual upon those old reliables Private Information and Personal Knowledge.

It is in the country of his birth where he is best remembered. Canada has a thriving Guggisberg Institute, devoted to matters of education.

The doings of the West African Divisions in Burma are set out in *The History of The Royal West African Frontier Force* by Colonel Haywood and Brigadier Clarke, Gale & Polden, 1964.

INDEX

212

Jebbe, Lieut.-Colonel Joshua, RE, designs Pentonville Prison 170
Jervois, Colonel W.F.D., 76

Kempt, General Sir James, 20,58,63
Kinglake, A.W., 138-9
Kingston, G.S., 74
Kipling, Rudyard, in Japan, 136
Kitchener, FM Earl, 15,128-9,147, 163,165,173,181 et passim

Lake, Captain H.A., 101
Lancaster, Joseph, school reformer, 26
Landmann, Herr, Professor at RMA, 11
Lefebure, Captain Charles, killed at Cadiz, 24
Lewis, Colonel, RE, on Rideau Canal, 56
Light, Colonel William, founder of Adelaide, 5,71 et seq.
Linant Bey, French engineer in Egyptian service, 142,154
Liverpool, Lord, Prime Minster 1812, 39

Macdonald, Major, Sinai resident in 1868, 129
Macdonnell, Colonel 'Red George', Canadian soldier, 35
Machell, Lieutenant, RE, assists Charles Pasley with his school, 26
McGowan, Ned, 111
McGregor, 'Rob Roy', 5,130,142-7
MacGregor, Gregor, 'Prince of Poyais', 70
McKay, Thomas, Rideau Canal contractor, 47,50
Mackenzie, Alexander, 107,119
McTaggart, John, with By on the Rideau Canal, 46 et seq., 62,65
Madras system of education, 26
Maida, battle of, 20
Malcolm, Admiral Sir Pulteney, 16
Mann, Major-General Gother, 27,36,40
Marlborough, John Churchill, 1st. Duke of, 10

Marryat, Captain Frederick, RN, 13,67,86
Martello Towers, 21
Mehemet Ali, Pasha of Egypt, 72,141 et seq.
Melbourne, 74
Moberley, Walter, in British Columbia, 118
Montagu, Duke of, Master-General of the Ordnance 1741 10
Moody, Colonel R.C., RE, 108 et seq.
Mougel Bey, 144-5
Mulcaster, Lieutenant, killed at Badajoz, 3,16
Mulcaster, General, 66

Napier of Magdala, FM Lord, 16,82, 130
Napier, Commodore (Later Admiral Sir Charles) 142,153-4
Napier, General Sir Charles, 73
Napoleon III, Emperor of the French, 169,177
Nelson, Vice-Admiral Viscount, 19
New Westminster, founding of, 115
North-West Company, 107

Ogilvy, J.D.B., of Hudson's Bay company, murdered by Bella Coola Indians 121
Orr, Major-General Charles, 97,99, 101
Ottawa, 67

Page, Captain Hyde, designs Grand Shaft, 186
Palestine Exploration Fund, 126
Palmer, Major-General H.S., 5,105-137
Palmer, Professor E.H., in Sinai survey 1868, 127 et seq.
Parkes, Sir Harry, 133 et seq.
Pasley, Major-General Sir Charles, 3,16 et seq. et passim.
Pattison, Lieut.-Colonel James, at RMA, 11 et seq.
Pennyfeather, Mr., Rideau Canal contractor, 57